D0011736

ANCIENT STORIES OF THE
QUICHE INDIANS OF GUATEMALA

POPOL WUH

ILUSTRATED WITH DRAWING FROM
THE MAYAN CODICES

Adaptation, Notes, Vocabulary and English Version
by
Albertina Saravia E.

EDITORIAL
Piedra Santa

S

Title in Spanish
POPOL VUH, Antiguas historias de los indios quichés de Guatemala

Sixth reprint in English: 2003

Digital cover design by
Raúl Piedra Santa Díaz

Monument from Site Q showing an elite ballplayer, in the classical Maya position, down on one padded knee. Guiding the giant rubber ball with his clenched fist to hit the leading edge of his ribbed wooden ball deflector. The semi-circular flaps on each side are thick cloth or leather to protect his thighs. The ball is decorated with the bar-and-dot numeral nine. The meaning of this measurement is not yet deciphered. (Caption provided by Nicholas Hellmuth)

5a. calle 7-55, zona 1
Tels/Fax: 279 1189 al 279 1193
e-mail: editorialps@yahoo.com
Guatemala, Centro América

Editorial y Distribuidora en El Salvador
Avenida Olímpica # 3428
entre 65 y 67 Av. Sur
Tels.: 223 5502, 223 4440 Fax: 223 6564
E-mail: piedra_santa@navegante.com.sv
San Salvador, El Salvador

ISBN: 84-8377-095-4
Código: 113-0036

Un producto centroamericano impreso
en los talleres de KOSMOCOLOR.

DEDICATED

to my father

Adalberto A. Saravia
who taught me to love the
POPOL WUH

ACKNOWLEDGMENT

The English version of the POPOL VUH is a traslation from the Spanish edition published by Editorial Porrua, Hnos. México, 1965, by the same author. The text is revised and improved, and the vocabulary is increased.

Many thanks to the following persons who reviewed the English version:

Ruth Henderson De Grau. B. A., Blufftone College, Ohio. Former professor of English at the I.GA. (Instituto Guatemalteco Americano) Guatemala.

Margaret McClear. Ph. D. in Spanish Literature. Professor of Literature at the University of Commerce, Texas.

George Jesse Lukens. B. A. University of Missouri. M. A. University of Michigan. Professor of English at Facultad de Humanidades, Universidad de San Carlos de Guatemala, since 1950.

The editors wish to express their thanks to Dr. Leland W. Cross who are their request reviewed the English version of the POPOL WUH by Albertina Saravia E.

Dr. Cross is a graduate from the University of Michigan, the Universidad de las Américas, México, and George Washington University, and has been Cultural Attache of the U.S.A. Embassy in Guatemala.

NOTES

When I was a little girl I used to listen spellbound to the stories from the *Popol Wuh* with which my father entertained us. When I was twelve years old I asked him to give me the book to read. He gave it to me, but I must confess that I did not understand it. It was too confusing for me with so many repetitions, and even if I read it through to the end, I could not make head or tail of it. I was left with the desire that someone would write a version understandable to everyone who read it. Years passed by, and since nobody wrote it, I decided to do it myself. After working eight years on it the result is this adaptation of drawings from the Mayan Codices and the *Popol Wuh* text.

The legends are from the revised version by Ximenes placed at the beginning of his HISTORIA DE LA PROVINCIA DE SAN VICENTE DE CHIAPA Y GUATEMALA, Vol. I, published by the "Sociedad de Geografía e Historia de Guatemala", in 1929.

From this text I omitted the repetitions and arranged some sentences in order to make it easier to understand. I also used more modern terms to substitute archaic ones. The legends are complete except for the genealogies of the Quiche chiefs, which do not have a place in this type of work.

Imitating Rudyard Kiplig's THE JUNGLE BOOK, I give the name in Quiche followed by its meaning in English, for example: Coy, the Monkey; the Ahawab, the Lords; Xibalba, Hell; etc.

The wonderful descriptions of the scenes in the POPOL WUH that my father gave us, made a great impression on my imagination. The visions they had engendered were latent in my memory; I could see the scenes in my mind. That is why I wished to illustrate the text with drawings, and in order to know something about the people —their dresses and postures— of the pre-Columbian times, I studied the drawings of the Mayan Codices. I realized then that I could use these drawings to illustrate the text that I was working on. I had the necessary training to do so since I have been a teacher, and I always illustrated my lessons. I went to the National Museum where there are copies of the Mayan Codices. These Codices are the *Dresdensis,* the *Tro-Cortesianus* and the *Peresianus,* and are the only Mayan ones known to have been saved from destruction by man and time.

The pages in this book resemble those of the Codices and the size is, more or less, that of the *Codex Tro-Cortesianus*. The page number and initials of the copy of the Codex from which a drawing was taken are at the foot of the drawings, as follows: *Codex Tro-Cortesianus* (C.T.) *Codex Peresianus* (.CP.) *Codex Dresdensis* (C.D.). The part of the *Codex Tro-Cortesianus* known as *Codex Cortesianus* does not have numbered pages, and the drawings from this *Codex* have the initials (C.CT).

When I traced the drawings I did not copy the Mayan numbers or the hieroglyphics and other details which overload them. This was done in order that the drawings could be seen more clearly.

The pages are numbered with the Mayan numerical system and with the corresponding Arabian number.

While I was working on this adaptation I had in mind that my main purpose was to popularize the reading of a wonderful document of Latin American Indian literature, and to make known the Mayan drawings which are so plastic and so little known.

Upon reading this book it must be taken into account that the *Mayan Codices* and the *Popul Wuh* come from two different cultures and epochs: the first ones are from the Mayan Era before Columbus came to America; the second one is a Quiche document written during the Spanish domination. There is a difference approximately of 300 years between the two. That is to say, these two documents are not related.

I give the following data of the documents used in this work, and of the first translator and discoverer of the *Popol Wuh.*

THE QUICHES. The Quiche nation was one of the branches which descended from Mayan stock, and was one of the most powerful and civilized nations of Central America.

They resisted the Spaniards with great courage, but were finally overcome, and those who survived took refuge in the town known today as Santo Tomas Chichicastenango, where many of the descendants of the Quiches now live.

POPOL WUH. The *Popol Wuh* is a very important Quiche document that contains fragments of cosmogony, religion, mythology, traditions of the immigrations, and history of the Quiches.

It is supposed that it was transcribed in the Roman alphabet during the Spanish domination by one or more Quiche Indians who learned to read and write from the Spaniards. The name or names are unknown. It is possible that the ancient book mentioned in the *Popol Wuh* was written according to the Indian system, with drawings and hieroglyphics.

FRIAR FRANCISCO XIMENEZ. He was born in Exija province in Andalucía, Spain in 1666. He arrived in Guatemala in 1688. He belonged to the Order of the Friars of Saint Dominic and was a priest in Santo Tomas Chichicastenango from 1701 to 1703. He was an excellent linguist and possessed a good knowledge of the Quiche language. The Indians trusted him to the point of showing him the manuscript of the Quiche traditions, which is called today *Popol Wuh.* Ximenez copied the original in the Quiche language and translated it into Spanish. This copy is the one kept at the Newberry Library, Chicago, and is considered the original of the book. Ximenez wrote a revised transcription of the *Popol Wuh,* which is found at the beginning of his HISTORIA DE LA PROVINCIA DE CHIAPA Y GUATEMALA, already mentioned.

Friar Francisco Ximenez died around 1730.

MAYAN CODICES. The codices are pre-Columbian Mayan documents about astronomy, rituals and horoscopes, and are illustrated with drawings, hieroglyphics and numbers.

There are only three known Mayan codices: *Codex Dresdensis, Codex Tro-Cortesianus* and *Codex Peresianus.* The originals are in Dresden, Madrid and Paris, respectively.

A codex was made from the bark of a tree prepared in a special way. It was formed of long strips of bark folded like a screen. The pages were divided into two, three and sometimes four parts by horizontal colored lines and were enclosed by colored margins.

The size of the pages in the *Codex Tro-Cortesianus* and *Codex Peresianus* are almost the same: 9 1/4 inches long by 5 inches wide. The *Codex Dresdensis* is smaller, its pages being 8 inches long by 3 1/2 inches wide.

MAYAN NUMERS. The Mayan numerical system was vigesimal and used points and bars. The point (.) has a numerical value of one (1) and the bar (........) a numerical value of five (5). Combining and adding these two symbols, numbers could be written up to 19, as follows:

0	5	10	15
1	6	11	16
2	7	12	17
3	8	13	18
4	9	14	19

Numbers from 20 up required the use of their arithmetical system of positions in which values increase by 20. The vigesimal progression is: 1, 20, 400, 8,000, 160,000, etc. The Mayans followed this progression faithfully, except for the time computation, where the third position was 18 times the second position, instead of 20 times. This was to give a 360 value instead of 400. One of the most common symbols used to represent zero (0) was a conventional shell . For example: 40 was written . In the first position a shell was drawn to indicate zero (0) units, and two points in the second position to indicate two units of the second order.

PRONUNCIATION. *x:sh* as in *she;h:* strong as in *h*e; *j* same as *h;* *w* as in *w*agon. The word *WUH* is correctly written in modern Quiche. The sign (ʾ) following a letter in a Quiche word, indicates a glotalized sound.

Since this book is for popular purposes, I only wrote some of the Quiche words with the symbols representing their sounds, according to modern Quiche linguistics.

If this adaptation of the *Mayan Codices* to the *Popol Wuh* awakens the interest of the public to read these documents in their original versions, it will compensate my efforts. At the same time it will fulfill my aim, because I am convinced of the great importance that these stories of the Ancient Quiche Indians of Guatemala, have in the literature of the Americas.

Guatemala, October 1954

Albertina Saravia E.

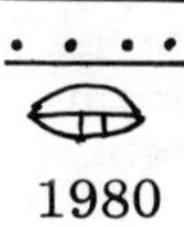

1980

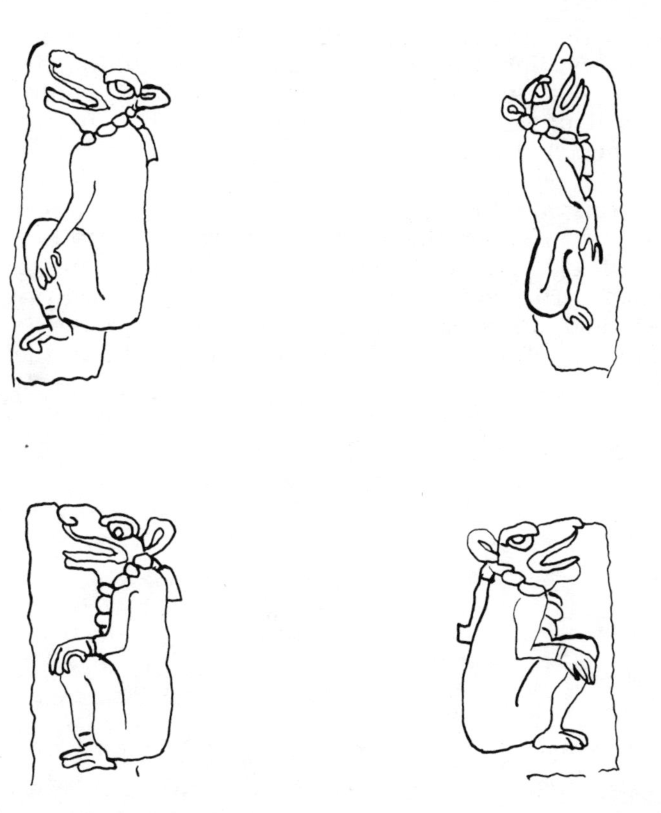

XXVI
C.T.

This is the beginning of the old stories of the people of Quiché, and we shall write and tell about the Creator and Maker who is Mother and Father of everything.

We write this in the time of Christianity because, even though we have the old and original book, it is no longer legible.

(to be continued)

After the lines and parallels of Heaven and Earth were made, everything was finished and divided into climates. When all was put in order, it remained divided into four parts, as if it were measured with a cord. This formed the four corners and four sides.

All this was finished and made perfect by the Creator and Maker of everything, the One who is Mother and Father of Life and Creation, He who gives us breath and movement, He who gives us Peace. He is the Light of His children and takes care of them, and maintains the Beauty that exists in Heaven and Earth, in the lakes and in the sea.

9 C.D.

Before the Creation there were neither men nor animals, birds, fish, crabs, trees, stones, holes, ravines, grass nor vines. The surface of the earth was hidden. There was only the sea and it was calm, and in the sky there was nothing which could make noise. There was not a thing that existed, nothing that had being, only the sea and the still water. There was only silence and tranquility in the darkness and the night. There only existed the Lord and Creator, K'ucumatz, Mother and Father of everything, and He lives in the water; and He is called Heart of Heaven, because He is there and there He lives. His Word came with the Lords Tepew and K'ucumatz. They talked, and deliberating, consulting, and discussing in the middle of that darkness, they created all the creatures.

44 C.D.

And there was manifested the creation of trees, and of life, and of all that was created by the Heart of Heaven, who is called Hurakan.

The first manifestation of Hurakan was called Caculha Hurakan, Lightning with One Leg. The second was called Chipi Caculha, The Smallest of Lightnings. And the third was called Raxa Caculha, Very Beautiful Lightning.

And these three manifestations are the Heart of Heaven.

XXII
C.T.

First were created the earth, the mountains, and the plains; the roads of water were divided, and there were many rivulets between the hills. In some places the water was detained and overflowed. In this way the high mountains appeared.

Then were made the animals, guardians of the woods: the deer, the bird, the puma, the jaguar, the snake, the serpent and the viper.

And they were given their homes and places to live in.

And they said:

"You, deer, will live and sleep in the ravines by the river bank; you will walk amid the pastures, and you will multiply yourself in the woods; you will walk on four feet and they will support you."

And they said to the big birds, to the small birds:

"You, birds, will live in the trees and vines, and there you will make your nests. There you will multiply yourselves and there you will clean the lice from your feathers."

And they all sought their homes just as the Creator commanded, and they inhabited Ulew, the Earth.

XXXI
C.T.

And having created all the birds and animals, the creators said to them:

"Talk and scream according to your kind; pronounce and praise our name; say that we are your Mothers and Fathers, as we are indeed. Speak, praise, invoke us! "

But even though this was commanded of them, they could not speak as humans; they only screamed, cackled and hissed.

XXIX
C.T.

They tried to put words together and hail the Creator, but could not; they were punished and since then their meat has been eaten by man.

The Makers tried to form other creatures. They made man of mud, but he was limp, and he could not move; because the mud was soft, that man was not good. He could speak, but he had no mind and he dissolved in the water.

Seeing this, the Creators destroyed their work, and consulted the soothsayers Xpiyacoc and Xmucane to find out how they could make man.

28 C.D.

The soothsayers made their divination, casting their lots with the corn and the tzite, the red beans:

"Thou, Sun! Thou, Moon! Join together, and tell us if it is well that the Creator carve man out of wood and if this man be he who must be nourished after being formed. Speak Thou, Corn! Speak Thou, Tzite! Thou, Sun! Thou, Creature! Thou, Corn! Thou, Tzite! "

The corn and the tzite spoke the truth in this way:

"You can whittle man, and your figures of wood shall speak".

XVII*
C.T.

Instantly men were made of wood. They multiplied themselves, and they had sons and daughters; but they were stupid, without hearts and minds; they walked over the earth, but they did not remember the Heart of Heaven.

Their hands were without blood and were not moist; their cheeks and feet were pale and dry, their flesh was yellow, and they moved awkwardly.

There were many of these men over the face of the Earth.

74 C.D.

The men of wood were punished because they did not remember their Creators and Makers. A heavy black rain of resin and tar fell from heaven, and they were deluged. In this way The Heart of Heaven destroyed them.

XXVI*
C.T.

The bird called Cotcowach went and gouged out their eyes. Another named Camalotz cut off their heads. The animal called Cotzbalam devoured their flesh. And the one called Tucumbalam broke their bones and nerves, and ground them into flour.

This was to punish men of wood because they forgot their Mothers and Fathers.

Then came all kinds of animals together with sticks and stones, and struck men's faces. And all began to speak: their grinding stones, griddles, plates, pots, dogs, and earthen jars: all struck them. And the dogs and the hens said:

"You bit us, and ate us; now we shall bite and eat you in return".

And the grinding stones said: "We worked all day, and we made *holi, holi, huqui, huqui,* as it sounds when we grind the corn. You tormented us."

XX
C.T.

When the dogs spoke they said:

"Why did you not fed us, and we only looked when you ate? You threw us out and a stick was always ready to strike us. You treated us this way because we could not speak. Why did you not look out for us? Now you will taste the teeth of our mouths, and we shall eat you."

The griddles and pots spoke to them in this maner:

"Pain and suffering you gave us. You burned our mouths and faces; we always had them blackened, and all the time we were on the fire. Now we shall burn you! "

And the stones on which pots are laid at the fire, said:

"You always put us on the fire giving us great pains; now we shall break your heads."

36. C.D.

The men of wood tried to save themselves from the deluge.

36 C.D.

Men were desperate, and attempting to find refuge they climbed over the top of their houses, but the houses fell apart. If they climbed the treetops, the trees cast them off. If they wanted to take refuge in the caves and holes, these closed their entrances.

XXV*
C.T.

In this way the men of wood were destroyed, and all that remains of them are the monkeys that live in the woods.

That is why Coy, the Monkey, resembles man.

XXXIV*
C.T.

The sky and the earth existed, but the light of the sun and the moon was dim.

Then a being called Wukub K'aquix was very proud of himself because of his wealth. Wukub K'aquix had two sons: Zipacna and Cab Rakan. Their mother was Chimalmat, the wife of Wukub K'aquix. The elder, Zipacna, fancied himself the propietor of the mountains because he created them in one night. His brother Cab Rakan moved and made the high mountains tremble. The sons of Wukub K'aquix were very proud of themselves.

In this way all of them showed their pride, and this seemed very evil to the two youths, Hun Ahpu and Xbalamque. They decided to kill them.

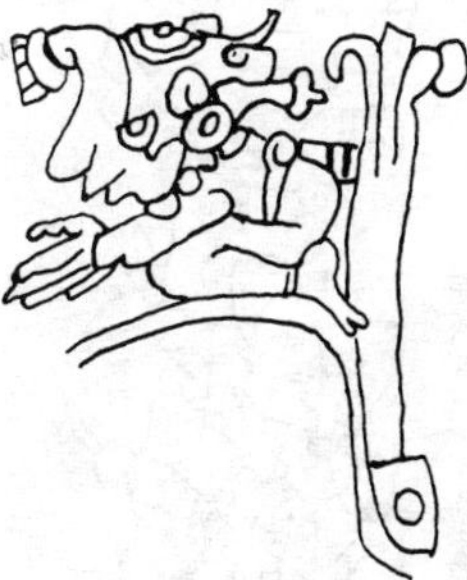

XXVIII
C.T.

Hum Ahpu and Xbalamque observed that Wukub K'aquix had a tree, and that he ate of its yellow berries every day to sustain himself. Taking along their blowguns, they went there quietly, and when they arrived at the foot of the tree they hid amid the grass.

15C.D.

Wukub K'aquix climbed the tree and Hun Ahpu shot him with his blowgun, breaking his jaw. Wukub K'aquix fell down screaming with pain.

44 C.D.

Hun Ahpu bent down to overpower Wukub K'aquix, but he seized Hun Ahpu by the arm, tore it from its socket, and took it home. When he arrived, he told his wife:

"Two demons dislocated my jaw with a shot from a blowgun. All my teeth are loose and I have a toothache. But I brought the arm of one of them. Hang it over the fire until the two demons come for it."

Chimalmat, Wukub K'aquix's wife, hung up the arm of Hun Ahpu over the smoke of the fire.

XXXIII*
C.T.

After thinking it over, Hun Ahpu and Xbalamque decided to talk with an old man and an old woman. They were so old that they were stooped. The youths said to them:

“Come with us to Wukub K’aquix’s house. He took Hun Ahpu’s arm with him. Use some tricks to overpower him.”

“Very well”, answered the old woman and the old man, “and we shall put your arm back into its place.”

• • • •

VI
C.T.

They found Wukub K'aquix sitting on his throne and he was screaming because his teeth gave him pain. The two old people passed by his house with the two boys playing behind them. Wukub K'aquix called them and asked them to cure him. The old ones pulled out the teeth, put grains of white corn in their place and Wukub K'aquix lost his lordly appearance. Then they pierced the pupils of his eyes and took all his silver ornaments. This is the way Wukub K'aquix perished. Chimalmat, his wife, died too.

After Hun Ahpu's arm was put back into its socket, the two youths said goodby to the elders.

In this manner they obeyed the orders of the Heart of Heaven.

67 C.D.

One day Zipacna was taking a bath at the edge of a river when he saw Four Hundred Youths dragging a big log that was so heavy they could scarcely move it. Zipacna helped them by carrying it alone. The boys were angered by his strength and decided to destroy him. They told Zipacna to make a big hole, and while working he heard their plan, and made a small cave on one side of the hole. When the hole was deep enough the youths threw a big log into it. Zipacna cried aloud when the log fell, but he was safe in the cave.

The boys were very glad, believing that Zipacna was dead.

C.TC.

The Four Hundred Youths were so glad that they said:

"Let us prepare our fermented corn beverage and within three days, when it is ready and when Zipacna is putrified, we shall celebrate our deed. We shall wait until the ants eat him, to be sure of his death. Then we can celebrate our feast without care."

C.TC.

When Zipacna heard this, he trimmed his hair and fingernails with his teeth, and the ants carried out the cuttings.

The Four Hundred Youths saw the ants carrying Zipacna's nails and hair. They were very happy and drank their corn beverage on the third day, and they became so intoxicated that they lost their senses.

C.TC.

Zipacna crept out of his hole and let the house fall over them. He beat them and killed all of them. When they died the Four Hundred Youths became stars and were called Motz, the Huddle.

Hun Ahpu and Xbalamque were very sad when they heard about the death of the Four Hundred Youths. They despised Zipacna in their hearts, and decided to punish him by killing him.

44 C.D.

To accomplish their plan Hun Ahpu and Xbalamque made the image of a crab and placed it in a cave under a big mountain. They went looking for Zipacna and when they found him they said:

"What is your food, young man?"

"Fish and crabs", answered he, "but I am very hungry. I have not eaten for three days."

"Come with us, Zipacna. We saw a big red crab in a cave."

XXXII*
C.T.

When they arrived at the place, they saw the crab with its big, red shell.

Zipacna was very happy when he saw it, and he said:

"I am so hungry that I wish I could eat it."

Zipacna fell down on his knees and tried to crawl into the cave, but the crab was climbing up. When Zipacna was almost inside and only his knees were out, the mountain fell on him and he was changed into stone.

In this way Zipacna, the elder son of Wukub K'aquix, the maker of the mountains, was defeated and killed by the two youths, Hun Ahpu and Xbalamque.

XX*
C.T.

The other one who was proud of himself was Cab Rakan, the second son of Wukub K'aquix. When Hurakan realized this, he called Hun Ahpu and Xbalamque and ordered them to destroy him.

Cab Rakan was moving and shaking the mountains when the two young men said to him:

"We saw a mountain, but it is so big that we could catch neither one nor two birds. You could help us by demolishing it, so we could catch birds."

"Very well", answered Cab Rakan, "I shall demolish it."

5 C.D.

"We shall go with you", said the boys, "and if there are birds we shall shoot them with our blowguns."

They shot the birds blowing through their blowguns without any clay pellets and Cab Rakan admired them for this. When the time came for eating they stopped and built a fire. They put the birds to roast on it, and they rubbed one of them with white clay. They turned the birds and their appetizing odor reached Cab Rakan's nostrils and he felt his mouth water. The boys gave him the bird they had rubbed with clay and he ate it. This proved to be his ruin and destruction.

XXXIV*
C.T.

When they had finished eating they strolled toward the sunrise, where the big mountain was. Cab Rakan did not have any strength left because of the clay on the bird he had eaten, and he could not demolish the mountain. The youths tied his hands and feet. Throwing him to the ground, they made a hole and buried him.

In this way Cab Rakan, the second son of Wukub K'aquix, was overpowered and killed by Hun Ahpu and Xbalamque.

XX
C.T.

Now we shall tell the name of Hun Ahpu and Xbalanque's father. It was Hun Hunahpu, whose parents were Xpiyacoc and Xmucane. Hun Hunahpu and his brother Wukub Hunahpu were born in the darkness of the night, before man was created, and before the Sun and the Moon existed.

Hun Hunahpu begot two sons by Xbaquiyalo: Hun Batz and Hun Chowen. Hun Hunahpu was an excellent father; he practiced very good habits, and he taught his two sons to play music,

XXXIV
C.T.

to paint,

XVII*
C.T.

to set precious stones, and to be silversmiths and sculptors.

10 C.P.

Hun Hunahpu and Wukub Hunahpu liked to play ball, and on one occasion the Ahawab of Xibalba, the Lords of Hell, Hun Came and Wukub Came, heard them and sent their messengers the Tucur, the Owls, to call them to their presence.

The Lords had great curiosity to see Hun Hunahpu's and Wukub Hunahpu's instruments of the ball game, but they hid them in the garret. They went with the messengers who guided the two toward the road to Xibalba, Hell, until they arrived where it was divided into four roads. The Black Road spoke and told them to go by him, and they went where the Lords were seated waiting for them.

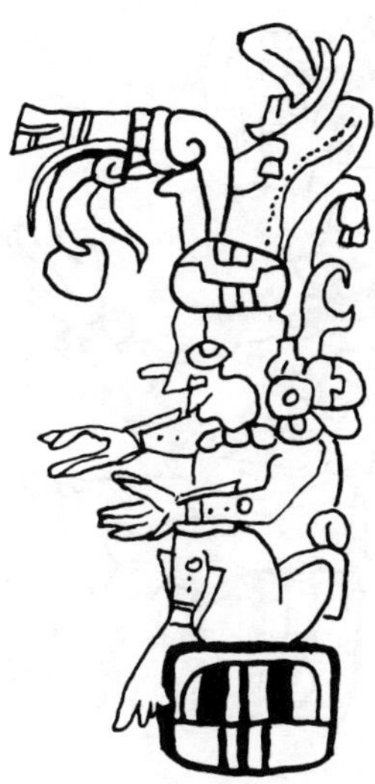

XXIII
C.T.

The first ones were two wooden figures, and Hun Hunahpu and Wukub Hunahpu greeted them first, but they did not answer back. The Lords laughed at them and invited them to sit on a bench that was a boiling hot stone. When they sat down their buttocks were burned, and they turned from one side to the other to avoid the heat.

XXIII
C.T.

When the Lords saw them trying to evade the heat of the stone, and that they had fallen into their trap, they began to laugh, and they laughed so much that they almost burst their blood vessels, and felt pain in their bones.

XXV*
C.T.

They took Hun Hunahpu and Wukub Hunahpu to the House of Darkness, full of gloom. The Ahawab, the Lords, sent them a pine stick and two cigars, and the porters said to them.:

"The Lords send you this tobacco and this pine stick and you must give them back whole tomorrow morning after smoking the cigars and burning the pine stick all night long."

And they were defeated because they finished the cigars and burned up the pine sticks.

XXX
C.T.

There were many places of punishment in Xibalba, Hell:

The first was the House of Darkness, full of gloom.

The second was the House of Cold or of Shivering for it was very cold.

The third was the House of the Jaguars, in which there were so many of those animals that they pushed one another.

The fourth was the House of Bats, in which there was no end to the bats that flew and screeched.

The fifth was the House of Knives, in which there were sharp and pointed obsidian knives that grated againts one another.

XXVI*
C.T.

After dawn the Ahawab, the Lords, sent for Hun Hunahpu and Wukub Hunahpu, and Hun Came and Wukub Came said to them:

"Where are the tobacco and the pine sticks we sent to you? "

"They are all gone, Sirs", they answered.

"Your days are ended and you shall die", sentenced the Ahawab of Xibalba, the Lords of Hell.

XXXII
C.T.

They cut them into pieces and buried them. Before burying them they cut off Hun Hunahpu's head and they put it in a fork of a barren tree by the road. As soon as the head was placed there, it disappeared and the tree gave forth fruit. Today we call this tree the calabash tree or gourd tree. The tree was so full of fruit that nobody could distinguish Hun Hunahpu's head among them.

The Lords of Hell thought of this tree as something miraculous and ordered everybody to keep away from it.

XVII*
C.T.

The daughter of Ahaw Cuchumaquic, called Xquic, heard how the formerly barren tree gave forth fruit. She was curious and wished to see it. When she saw the tree full of fruit, she said to herself:

"I shall not go without tasting one of these fruits. I am sure I shall not die."

She was thinking this when the head that was placed in the fork of the tree said:

"Do you really want of this fruit with all your heart? "

"Yes, I want it", the maiden said.

17 C.D.

"Stretch out your right hand", said the skull.

Xquic extended her right hand, and straightway the skull let its spittle fall into the maiden's hand. When she looked at it, nothing was on the palm. The skull said:

"The spittle that I threw to you is the mark of my descent that I leave to you. Go, walk up to Ulew, the Earth, and you will not die."

All this was accomplished by the order of Hurakan, Chipi Caculha and Raxa Caculha, who are the Heart of Heaven.

XIX*
C.T.

The young girl returned home having conceived Hun Ahpu and Xbalamque by virtue of the spittle.

When six months had passed Cuchumaquic observed his daughter, and noticed that she was pregnant. He then held council with the other Ahawab and told them:

"My daughter has proceeded with immodesty and she is disgraced."

The council condemned her to be taken away and to sacrifice her life, even when she defended herself by saying:

"My Lord and Father, I have not known man."

XVIII*
C.T.

Cuchumaquic did not believe what his daughter told him and called the four Ahawab Tucur, the four Lords Owl, and told them.:

"Take my daughter away; she has been lustful. Sacrifice her and bring her heart in a gourd."

The messengers took a gourd and a sharp knife to sacrifice the maiden with it.

XXIV*
C.T.

The messengers carried Xquic away.

The maiden said to the Tucur, the Owls:

"Do not take away my life. What happened was that when I went near the tree where Hun Hunahpu's head is, the skull spit in the palm of my hand, and that was all."

"We would like to spare your life", replied the messengers, "but what shall we put in the gourd to bring to the Lords? You know very well they ordered us to kill you, and to bring your heart to them."

6 C.D.

"Very well", said she, "but from now on your job shall be to announce death. My heart shall not be burned in front of the Ahawab. Throw in the gourd the sap of this tree."

A red sap gushed forth from the tree, and the Tucur, the Owls, gathered it in the gourd. The red sap coagulated and a heart shaped ball was formed.

The messengers brought that clot to the Lords instead of bringing Xquic's heart.

Xquic walked up to Ulew, Earth.

XXV*
C.T.

Hun Came and Wukub Came took the gourd, and grasped with three fingers the clot dripping blood. They ordered the servants to stir the fire. When they placed on it what they believed to be the heart, a sweet fragance rose from it. Everyone marveled at it.

The Tucur, the Owls, took the road toward Ulew, the Earth, having thus tricked the Lords of Hell, the Ahawab of Xibalba.

XI*
C.T.

Xmucane, the grandmother of Hun Batz and Hun Chowen, was at home when the young Xquic arrived and said to her:

"Here I am, my lady. I am your daughter in-law and the lesser of your daughters."

"Where do you come from? My sons died, but if it is true that you are my daughter-in-law take this net and go to the cornfield, and bring it full of corn."

"Very well", said the maiden Xquic, taking the net.

18 C.D.

The young girl went to the cornfield, but she found only a few stalks of corn without ears. The girl was very anxious and began to beg the help of the Ahaw, Guardian of Food. She took the red silk of an ear without picking it, and she put the silk into the net. Instantly the net was full of ears of corn and the animals helped the girl to carry it. When she was near the house she pretended to be carrying it. When the old woman saw the net full of ears she went to the cornfield, believing it destroyed, but she saw it was just like before. Coming back she said to the girl:

"This is proof enough that you are my daughter-in-law."

68 C.D.

Xquic gave birth to two sons: Hun Ahpu and Xbalamque.

Hun Batz and Hun Chowen hated their brothers and punished them frequently, so likewise did the grandmother Xmucane.

Every day the young ones had to bring birds to the house which they shot with their blowguns, and their brothers ate the birds without leaving anything for them.

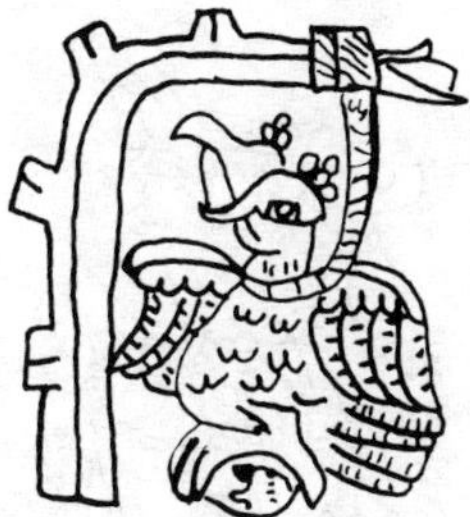

XXII*
C.T.

One day they arrived home bringing neither one nor two birds. The grandmother became furious. The boys said:

"We killed many birds, but they were caught in the tree and we cannot climb it because we are small. Our brothers can come with us, and help us by bringing them down."

"Very well", said Hun Batz and Hun Chowen, "we shall go with you early in the morning."

69. C.D.

They arrived at dawn where a big tree was. The two boys shot many birds with their blowguns, but none fell at the foot of the tree. Hun Batz and Hun Chowen climbed the tree and the tree trunk swelled so much that they could not come down. Their brothers said:

'Tie your loin cloths around your stomachs. Leave the long ends between your legs and pull them behind, and come down."

They did as directed, but the loin cloths were changed into tails and they were transformed into monkeys.

34 C.D.

Returning home Hun Ahpu and Xbalamque said to their grandmother:

"Grandmother, what could have happened to our brothers who, changing their faces, became animals? We shall try to call them, but it is very important that you do not laugh at them when you see them."

They went together to the woods, and the boys began to play their flutes and to sing the Hun Ahpu Coy song, Hun Ahpu's Monkey song, and playing their drums, they seated the grandmother near them.

In this way they called Hun Batz and Hun Chowen who came dancing to the time of the music of the instruments.

XX
C.T.

When the old woman saw their grimacing and their ugly faces, she began to laugh. She could not help it and the monkeys, ashamed, returned to the woods.

Continuing with the song and the flute, Hun Ahpu and Xbalamque started again to call their brothers, but the old woman laughed when she saw their stomachs and tails, and the monkeys returned once more to the woods.

34 C.D.

34 C.D.

Again they called the monkeys, who came dancing to the tune of flute and drum, but when they came the old woman could not help laughing, until finally they did not come back.

XII*
C.T.

Since ancient times the flute players, the singers, the painters and the carvers invoke and beg the help of Hun Batz and Hun Chowen who were changed into monkeys because they became proud and abused their brothers Hun Ahpu and Xbalamque.

XXXIII
C.T.

Hun Ahpu and Xbalamque remained with their grandmother and their mother and they performed many wonderful and marvelous deeds. They wanted to be well thought of by their mother and grandmother and the first thing they did was to work in the cornfield. And they said to them:

"Do not grieve, here we are, and we shall work in the cornfield so you can subsist."

They took their pointed sticks and axes and asked their grandmother:

"Grandmother, you come at midday to bring us our food."

"Very well", said she, "I shall take it there."

41 C.D.

When they arrived at the place where they planned to cultivate the corn they hit a tree with the axe and it crashed down, tearing up the vines and uprooting the other trees.

XXIII
C.T.

With a stroke of the planting stick all the land was cultivated and tilled.

It was a wonder to see how many of the trees and vines fell with only one stroke of the axe and how much of the land was tilled with only one stroke of the planting stick.

XXIV*
C.T.

They asked Xmucur, the Turtledove:

“Our grandmother will bring us our food. Sing at the moment you see her. In that way you will inform us of her coming. Then we shall take the stick and the axe.”

“Very well”, said the bird.

They amused themselves shooting with their blowguns.

As soon as the turtledove sang, one of them threw splinters of wood on his head, and taking the axe, he pretended to be cutting down the trees.

XXI
C.T.

The other one grasped earth with his hand and smeared his face with it. He took the planting stick and pretended to be tilling the soil.

When the grandmother arrived they ate as if they had worked a great deal and then returned home.

XV*
C.T.

Next day they went again to the cornfield and they found that all the trees were standing again and the soil was as before tilling it.

Trying to cultivate their cornfield once more they struck again with the axe and all the trees fell.

XXII
C.T.

With a stroke of the stick the soil was tilled. And they said:

"We shall watch during the night. In this way perhaps we can catch the one who is doing us damage."

XIX
C.T.

Taking their arms, they went to the cornfield and they hid themselves, watching.

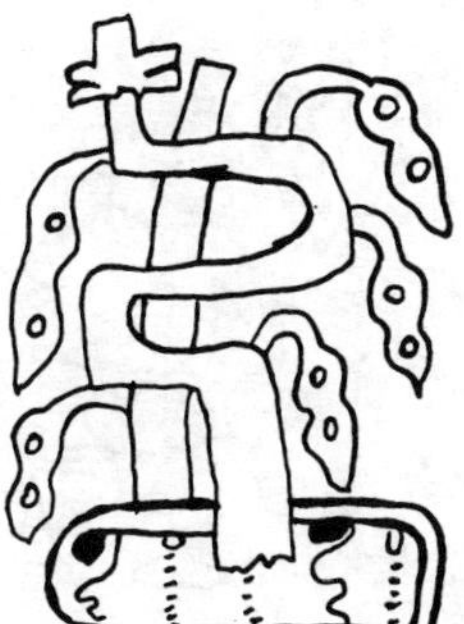

XXXII
C.T.

At midnight all the animals gathered together and said:

"Rise up, trees! Rise up, vines!"

XXXIII
C.T.

XX
C.T.

And moving under the trees and vines the small animals and the big animals approached the place where Hun Ahpu and Xbalamque were. A puma and a jaguar, coming in front of them, did not let the youths catch them.

XVII
C.T.

14.C.D.

When a rabbit and a deer passed together the youths wanted to catch them.

X
C.T.

They seized the tails, but the rabbit and the deer pulled away leaving their tails in their hands. That is why both have short tails.

They could catch neither the gray fox, nor the coyote, nor the coati.

XXXV
C.T.

At last they caught the mouse and, squeezing its neck, tried to choke it and they burned its tail in the fire. That is the reason why mice have protuding eyes and do not have hair on their tails.

The mouse said to Hun Ahpu and Xbalamque:

"Do not kill me. Your business is not to plant the cornfield. You must know that the belongings of your fathers are kep in the garret of your home. They consist of the instruments with which they played ball: the ring, the gloves, and the rubber ball. Now give me something to eat."

The youths alloted the mouse its food: corn, pepper seeds, beans, cacao and the foods which are kept in the houses.

XXIII*
C.T.

When they arrived home, carrying the mouse hidden, they begged their mother and grandmother for something to eat and water to drink. But the youths deceived them because they had drunk beforehand the water which was kept in an earthen jar.

XXVII
C.T.

The grandmother carried the earthen jar to the brook, but Xan, the Mosquito, bored a hole into it. She tried to plug the hole through which the water spurted, but she could not.

Later on Hun Ahpu and Xbalamque sent their mother to find out why their grandmother did not return with the water.

XXXV
C.T.

While the youths pretended to eat the mouse climbed to the garret and cut the rope. The instruments of the ball game fell down, and the boys gathered them up, and hid them.

Afterwards, they went to the brook where their mother and their grandmother were, and plugging the hole in the earthen jar, they returned home all together.

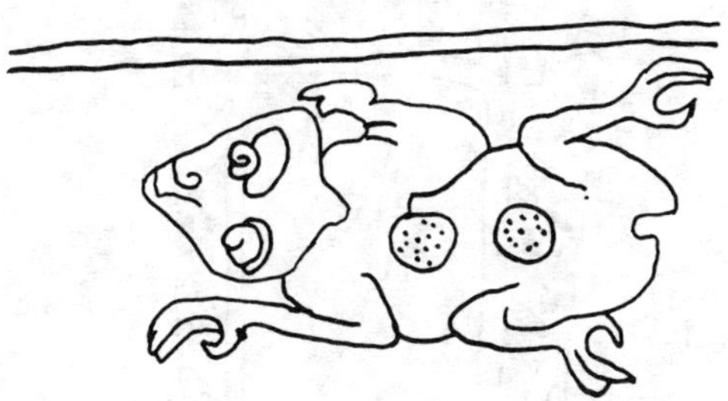

XXIV
C.T.

The boys were very happy and began to play ball. The Ahawab of Xibalba, the Lords of Hell, heard the noise and the running. They sent their messengers the Ahawab Tucur, the Lords Owl, to call them and they gave the message to their grandmother. She was worried, and sent a louse with the message to her grandsons. The louse encountered a youth called Tamazul, the Toad, who said to him: "Where are you going? "

"I carry a message in my stomach to the boys who are playing ball in the court."

"I see that you are tired and cannot run anymore. If you want I can swallow you, and I shall run to take you there", said the Toad. "See how I can run" added the Toad.

"Very well", said the louse.

And swallowing the louse, the Toad ran.

XXVII
C.T.

When Tamazul, the Toad, was tired he met Zaquicaz, the Snake:

"Where are you going, Tamazul? " said the Snake.

"I carry a message in my stomach", "replied the Toad.
"I see that you are tired and cannot walk any more", said the Snake, "come, Tamazul; I shall swallow you, in this way you can arrive quickly."

Saying this Zaquicaz, the Snake, swallowed Tamazul, the Toad.

Since then toads have been the food of snakes.

36 C.D.

The snake went running on the road and when she was tired she met Wac, the Hawk, who swallowed her and arrived quickly where the boys were playing.

Since then hawks have eaten as their food the snakes that slide over the fields.

7 C.D.

The boys were playing, throwing the ball to each other, when the bird sang and said: "Wac c'o! Wac c'o! Here is the Hawk! Here is the Hawk! "

Shooting with their blowguns, the boys hit the bird in one eye and the hawk fell down. He said:

"Cure my eye first, and afterwards I shall give you the message which I carry in my stomach."

The boys cured him with a bit of rubber from the ball. The hawk vomited the snake.

XXXII
C.T.

The boys said to Zaquicaz, the Snake:

"Tell us the message."

"I carry it in my stomach", replied the snake.

And Zaquicaz, the Snake, vomited Tamazul, the Toad.

They said to the Toad:

"Tell us your message."

3 C.D.

"I bring the message here, in my stomach", said Tamazul, the Toad.

He wanted to vomit, but could not throw up the louse. This provoked the boys, who gave him a kick and tore his mouth trying to open it. That is why since then toads have fallen rumps and large mouths. At last the boys opened the mouth of the toad and pulled out the louse which was stuck in the teeth of the toad. They said to the louse:

"Tell us the message", and the louse gave them the message from their grandmother.

The boys returned home to say goodby to their grandmother and their mother. They planted some canes in the house yard to be a token that they were alive. Then they went toward Xibalba, Hell. From then on the custom of planting canes in the house yards was established.

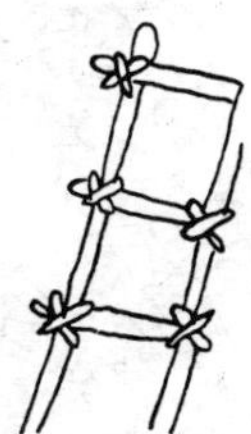

34 C.D.

They went to the road to Xibalba, Hell, carrying their blowguns, and descended the steep steps quickly. They passed two rivers, one of matter and the other of blood, without setting foot in them as they crossed them on their blowguns. They came to a crossing of four roads: a red one, another black, white the other, and yellow the last one.

They sent Xan, the Mosquito, to find out the names of the Ahawab of Xibalba, the Lords of Hell. They said to it:

"Go, see, and bite all the Lords who are seated, and from now on your food shall be the blood of the persons whom you bite on the roads."

48 C.D.

When the mosquito bit the Lords they revealed their names by asking each other who had bitten them. Xan, the Mosquito, returned and repeated the names to Hun Ahpu and Xbalamque, who went to the place where the Lords were seated.

Truthfully, Xan the Mosquito was not real. It was only a hair that Hun Ahpu pulled off his face and made into a shape like a mosquito. It was sent to find out the Lords' names.

47 C.D.

The boys said to the Lords of Hell, the Ahawab of Xibalba:

"We will not hail the first two, as they are only wooden figures, but we shall hail you: Hun Came, Wukub Came, Xiquiripat, Cuchumaquic, Alhalpuh, Ahalcana, Chamiabak, Chamiaholom, Xic, Patan, Quicre, Quicrixkak."

Not a single name was missed.

46 C.D.

The Ahawab were displeased and invited them to sit down.

"Oh, no", said the boys, "that bench is a hot stone! We shall not sit on it."

"Well then", said the Lords, "go rest yourselves in the guest house."

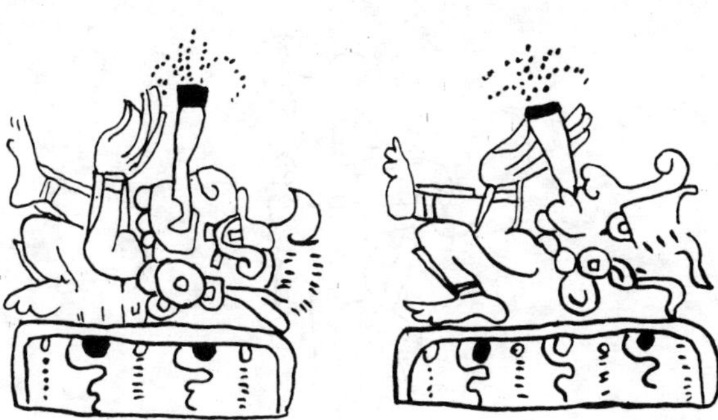

XXXIV*
C.T.

They were taken to the House of Darkness where the messengers brought them two pine sticks and two cigars, and warned them that they had to give them back whole in the morning, having burned them all night. The boys took two macaw feathers and put them on the pine sticks, and on the end of the cigars they placed two fireflies. The cigars and pine sticks glowed all night as if they were burning.

XXVIII
C.T.

The Ahawab were astonished to see the cigars and pine sticks whole. They invited the youths to play ball. First they played with a puma's head and afterwards with Hun Ahpu and Xbalamque's rubber ball.

The Lords pondered how to overcome the boys and said to them:

"Take these four gourds and bring them tomorrow full of flowers."

They were taken to the House of Knives, but these did not harm them.

The boys called all kinds of ants, the razor ants, the thigh ants, who obeyed them and went to the garden where the guardians were careless. They cut and brought the flowers.

50 C.D.

The messengers of Xibalba, Hell, said to the boys:

"The Lords command you to bring the flowers this moment."

When they arrived in front of the Lords they offered them the four gourds full of flowers.

The Ahawab summoned the guardians and reprimanded them because they let the boys steal the flowers, and in punishment they tore their mouths.

VI
C.T.

The Ahawab, the Lords, played ball with Hun Ahpu and Xbalamque for a while and agreed to continue the match on the following morning.

That night they were sent to the House of Cold. That house was too cold, but in the morning the youths were safe and sound because they made a fire with some logs to keep the cold away.

The messengers arrived in the morning to see if they were already dead. The Lords were discouraged to see that they could not overcome the youths, and they marveled each day at the wonders performed by Hun Ahpu and Xbalamque.

8 C. D.

Next night they were sent to the House of Jaguars, in which there were countless numbers of them.

"Do not bite us", they commanded them, "your food shall be bones."

Hun Ahpu and Xbalamque threw them some bones and the jaguars began to chew them. When the guardians heard the noise they believed the boys were dead. But the next day they found them without harm. The Ahawab of Xibalba, the Lords of Hell, marveled at that.

The following night they were sent to the House of Fire, but it did not harm them, and they came out very handsome the next morning.

XXIII
C.T.

The next night they were sent to the House of Bats in which there were great numbers of them.

Hun Ahpu and Xbalamque slept inside their blowguns and though the bats flew around them, they could not bite them. Hun Ahpu wanted to ascertain if dawn had come and looked out of his blowgun when Camasotz, the Bat of Death, cut off his head, leaving only the body.

The bats placed Hun Ahpu's head in the ball court.

XXI
C.T.

Xbalamque called all the animals, the large ones and the small ones, to help him make Hun Ahpu's head. All of them answered the call.

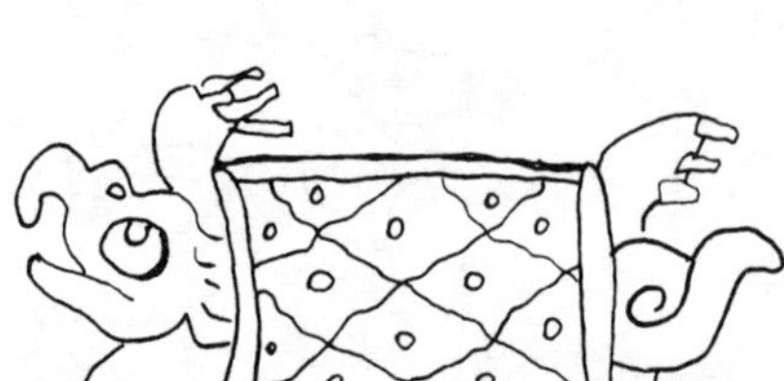

C.TC.

Coc, the Turtle, arrived the last, waddling as he came. Taking the turtle, Xbalamque carved from its shell Hun Ahpu's head. It came out a perfect head after carving the mouth and the eyes.

This was made with great wisdom because that was the will of Uc'ux Cah, the Heart of Heaven.

When it was finished they put it on Hun Ahpu's body and the head could speak.

XXXV
C.T.

While they were making Hun Ahpu's head, they realized that dawn was coming and they ordered C'uch, the Buzzard, to darken the sky. He did so by stretching out his wings and though four times dawn approached, four times the buzzard darkened the sky.

That is why nowadays, when the buzzard stretches out its wings when it is still dark, it is taken as the sign of approaching dawn.

When day broke, the two youths were well.

34 C.D.

After they placed Hun Ahpu's head over the ball court, the Lords wanted to celebrate the defeat of the two youths and they played ball.

5 C.P.

Xbalamque threw the ball and it rolled down to a tomato plant under which was a rabbit that ran away, and the Lords went after it, believing that it was the ball. Xbalamque had talked beforehand to the rabbit and told it what to do.

The ball court was empty and Xbalamque took Hun Ahpu's head and put it on his body. Taking the head of the turtle he placed it, instead of the real one, in the ball court.

The Lords, the Ahawab, were full of wonder at the sight of what had happened to Hun Ahpu.

37 C.D.

Hun Ahpu and Xbalamque did not die in any of these tortures.

At last, the Ahawab of Xibalba, the Lords of Hell, made a big bonfire in a hole, and called the two youths. When Hun Ahpu and Xbalamque were in front of it they faced each other, and stretching out their arms, leaped into the bonfire.

They ground their bones and cast them into the river, but the river did not carry them away. Instead, the bones went down to the bottom where they were changed back into two handsome youths.

XVII
C.T.

The youths showed themselves several times. On the fifth day the people of Xibalba saw two men and they hunted them all over the river until at last they came out wearing the clothes of the poor, dirty and ragged. They played and danced different kinds of dances, among them the dance of the Puhuy, the Owl, the dance of Cux, the Weasel, the dance of Iboy, the Armadillo, the dance of Xtzul, the Centipede, and the dance of Chitic, the One Who Walks on Stilts. They burned animals, persons, and various things, and changed them back without any harm. And they cut themselves into pieces, and came back to life.

XVII
C.T.

The people of Xibalba were full of wonder and fear to see such marvelous deeds and went to Hun Came and Wukub Came to tell them about the youths. The Lords sent their messengers to bring the boys to them in order to witness their performances.

Hun Ahpu and Xbalamque pretended reluctance to go to the Lords, but the messengers overpowered them and forced them to go.

"Do your dances and your plays", commanded the Ahawab of Xibalba.

When they started to dance and to sing all the people of Xibalba, Hell, gathered to see them.

13 C.D.

And a Lord, an Ahaw, said to them:

"Cut my dog into pieces and bring it back to life."

The youths took the dog, cut it into pieces and brought it back to life. The dog wagged its tail, happy to be alive again.

XXIX*
C.T.

"Very well", said another of the Lords, "now burn my house".

The house burned with everybody inside it, but no one came to harm. The boys left it as it was before.

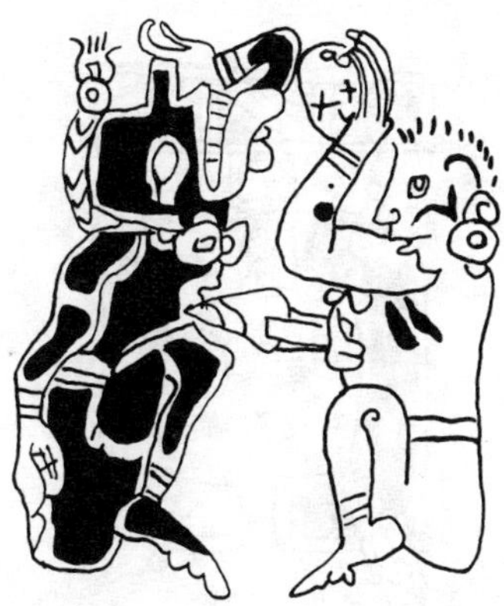

VII
C.T.

"Very well", said the Lords, "grasp one of these men, cut him to pieces and bring him back to life."

They grasped one of the crowd, cut him to pieces and the next moment they brought him back to life.

"Very well, now cut yourselves to pieces", said the Lords.

Xbalamque grasped Hun Ahpu, cut him to pieces and brought him back to life. When the Lords saw such marvelous deeds they wanted to be cut to pieces themselves and brought back to life. The boys cut them to pieces but did not bring them back to life.

And in this way the Ahawab of Xibalba, the Lords of Hell, were overpowered by Hun Ahpu and Xbalamque.

56 C.D.

These are the deeds and wonders of Hun Ahpu and Xbalamque, and this was the cause of the old woman's crying in front of the canes they left planted. These canes dried up when they died and sprouted again when they came back to life. The grandmother was very happy to see the canes sprouting again and burned *pom* incense in the middle of the house. From then on this custom was established.

After overpowering the Lords of Hell, the Ahwab of Xibalba, Hun Ahpu and Xbalamque went up to Heaven, and one of them was stationed as the Sun and the other as the Moon. Afterwards the Four Hundred Youths slain by Zipacna were placed as stars.

8 C.D.

The time for the creation of man grew nearer, and the Ahaw Tepew and the Ahaw K'ucumatz searched for the substance that was to be the flesh of man.

They held council among themselves and deliberated as to which way they were to make man, since the last one had been imperfect.

When they were seeking the material that could be used for the flesh and blood of man, it was revealed to them in the following manner:

6 C.P.

Four animals told the Creators and Makers about the yellow and the white ears of corn. These four animals were: Yak, the Gray Fox, Utiw, the Coyote, Quel, the Small Parrot, and Hoh, the Crow.

Grandmother Xmucane ground this yellow corn, and this white corn, and made a drink and a meal from which the flesh and blood of man were created. Of this same substance his hands and feet were made.

The Ahawab Tepew and K'ucumatz created our first fathers and mothers from corn.

23 C.D.

The first man to be created was Balam Quitze, Jaguar of Sweet Laughter. The second was Balam Ak'ab, Jaguar of the Night. The third was Mahucutah, Not Brushed. The fourth was Iqui Balam, Jaguar of the Moon.

They were very happy when they woke up and found their wives beside each one of them.

Balam Quitze's wife was called Caha Paluna. Standing Water Falling from Above.

19 C.D.

The second one was called Chomiha, Beautiful and Chosen Water, wife of Balam Ak'ab.

21. C.D.

The third one was called Tzununiha, Water of Hummingbirds, wife of Mahucutah.

21. C.D.

K'aquixaha, Water of the Macaw, was the name of Iqui Balam's wife.

And those four men were our first fathers, and those are the names of the women from whom we, the Quiches, descend.

20 C.P.

They multiplied themselves in the East in the time of darkness, before there were sun and light. The Ahawab, the Lords, prayed continually, raising their faces to the sky. And they said:

"Oh, Thou, who art Creator and Maker! Look at us, hear us, leave us not, forsake us not! Thou, Heart of Heaven and of Earth! Give us our descendants forever! When there is light, give us good and wide roads, give us quiet and peace, give us good life and customs, and being. Thou, Hurakan, Chipi Caculha, Raxa Caculha, Tepew, K'ucumatz, Who formed us, Who made us Thy children! "

The ones who prayed were Balam Quitze, Balam Ak'ab, Mahucutah and Iqui Balam.

25 C.D.

During this time our first fathers did not have idols made of stone or wood and many of the people went with them to find some. Having arrived at the place called Tulan, they found their idols there.

A messenger from Xibalba, Hell, said to them:

"This is your Idol, the one who will sustain you, and the one who truly represents your Creator and Maker! "

Balam Quitze carried the first idol to appear, Tohil, on his back in a *cacaxte.*

27 C.D.

Balam Ak'ab carried Awilix, the second one to appear.

28 C.D.

Mahucutah carried the third one, Hacawitz.

26 C.D.

Nicahtacah was the name of the one carried by Iqui Balam.

IV
C.T.

The Quiches, those of Tamub, and those of Ilocab, accompanied Tohil, and these were the names of the three Quiche Families.

Many were the ones who came out of Tulan, the white people and the black people. Their language was changed and each spoke in a different way and they could not understand one another.

They did not have fire during this time, but Tohil created it and gave it to them. The people warmed themselves with the fire and they were very happy at the comfort it gave them.

35 C.D.

The fire was burning, and very bright, when a heavy rain and hail fell that put it out.

Balam Quitze and Balam Ak'ab asked Tohil to give them fire again and Tohil created it by shuffling his foot in his sandal. Balam Quitze and Balam Ak'ab, Mahucutah and Iqui Balam warmed themselves by it and were very happy.

45 C.D.

The heavy shower of rain and hail had put out the fire of the people of the other tribes, who, shivering from the cold, went to Balam Quitze, Balam Ak'ab, Mahucutah and Iqui Balam to ask them for fire. The four gave it to them under the condition of being united with them, and the tribes accepted this condition.

But there was a tribe, that of the Cakchiqueles, who would not ask for the fire. They stole it under the cover of the smoke.

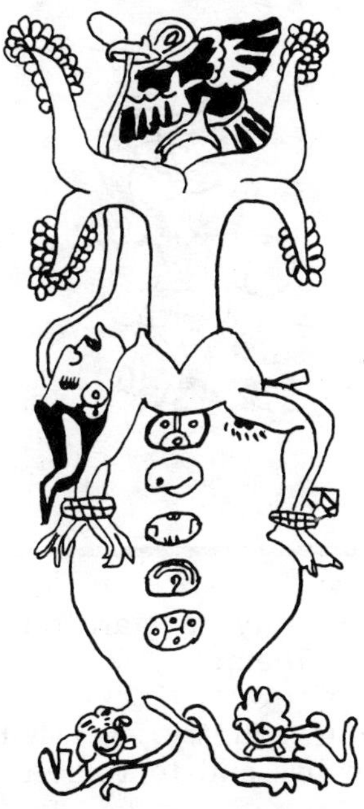

3 C.D.

The tribes that gave themselves up to be overcome were the ones that asked for the fire, and they shed blood from their sides and armpits when they were sacrified before Tohil.

XVIII*
C.T.

When they were ready to start their journey there in the East, Tohil said to them:

"This is not our country; we shall see where it is convenient for us to live and to toil. All of you must give thanks."

They pierced their ears and elbows with sticks, and this was their way of giving thanks to the gods.

34 C.D.

They wept copiously when they left Tulan, and they took turns watching for *Icok'ij,* the star they had as a token for the sunrise.

When they crossed the sea the waters parted and they passed over some stones.

All of them were sad. They were fasting and practicing abstinence from their wives, and great was their sorrow when their idols said to the four:

"Let us go away from here to a concealed place. Dawn is very near."

They hid the idols in the ravines.

16 C.D.

17 C.D.

In the midst of this confusion they saw *Icok'ij,* Venus, the star which was the guide and herald of the sun, and feeling very happy they burned their incense they brought with them from the East.

Then the sun shone and all the small and large animals rejoiced in it. The first to sing was Queletzu, the Parrot.

16 C.D.

16 C.D.

All the animals rejoiced; the birds stretched out their wings, and all turned their eyes to the point where the Sun was rising.

Balam Quitze, Balam Ak'ab, Mahucutah and Iqui Balam burned *pom* and they went dancing toward the place where the Sun was appearing while they shed sweet tears of happiness.

Then the idols were turned into stone.

XXIII*
C.T.

They were at Hacawitz Mountain when dawn came.

They began to search for the female of the deer and of the birds, to offer them to the idols.

25 C.D.

The Sacrificers offered the blood from the throats of the animals to Tohil, placed it in the mouth of the Idol, and the stone spoke.

V*
C.T.

Balam Quitze, Balam Ak'ab, Mahucutah and Iqui Balam disappeared from the sight of the people. They were roaming the mountains and brought to their wives and sons honey combs, horse flies and wasps to eat, but no one knew where they lived.

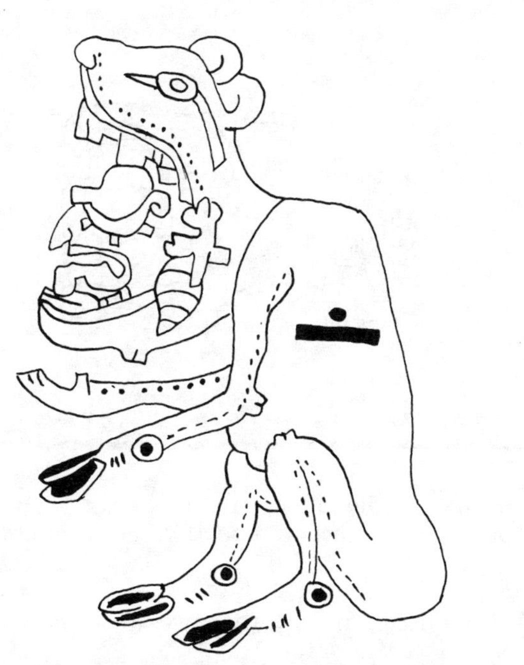

The tribes heard the gray foxes, coyotes, jaguars and pumas screaming, howling, and roaring from the mountain tops. The Sacrificers, disguised as animals, imitated the animal noises, and so the people were frightened. They kidnapped the people of the tribes and sacrificed them before the idols. In this way began the destruction of the tribes.

The people thought that the animals had devoured them as they saw only the footprints of the jaguars and those of other animals.

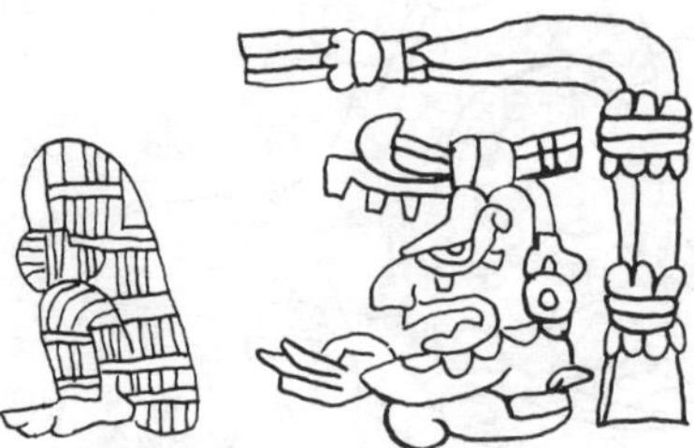

XII*
C.T.

When the people of the tribes began to wonder about the footprints, they gathered to take counsel about it. They said:

"What could it mean, that we are killed one by one, we, the people of the tribes? "

Already there were many dead when they realized it.

VI
C.T.

“Where are the Sacrificers and Worshipers in order to follow their footprints? ” said the tribes.

And they started to follow the footprints of the Worshipers and Sacrificers.

XXII
C.T.

The Sacrificers and Worshipers Balam Quitze, Balam Ak'ab, Mahucutah and Iqui Balam sacrificed the people they kidnapped from the roads and offered their blood to Tohil, Awilix and Hacawitz.

34 C.D.

The people were looking for the footprints when it began to rain and there was so much mud that they could not continue the search.

The tribes moved away from that mountain where men were killed and sacrificed before the Idol.

33. C.D.

The tribes gathered together once more and took counsel about what they had to do in order to overcome the Sacrificers. The first decision was to win the favor of Tohil, Awilix and Hacawitz, who had been seen in the guise of youths taking their baths in the river.

36 C.D.

They sent two beautiful maidens, daughters of Lords, to wash their garments at the edge of the river as a way to seduce the youths.

The two maidens went to the river and each of them disrobed herself. They started to wash their clothes when Tohil, Awilix and Hacawitz approached them.

The maidens were ashamed of their nakedness and told the gods why they were washing there. Tohil, Awilix, and Hacawitz offered to give them a token to prove to the Lords that they had seen them.

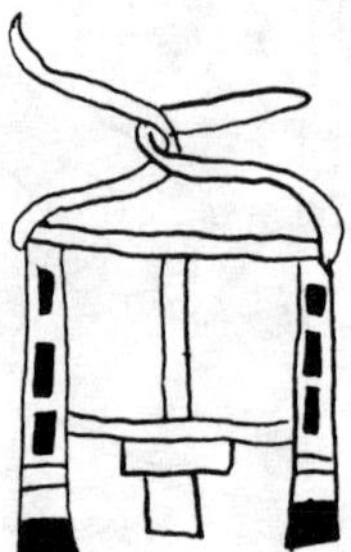

XXI
C.T.

Tohil, Awilix and Hacawitz said to Balam Quitze, Balam Ak'ab and Mahucutah:

"Take a piece of cloth and paint on it the image of your being."

They took a piece of cloth and Balam Quitze painted a jaguar on the first one. Balam Ak'ab painted an eagle on the second one, and Mahucutah painted horseflies and wasps on the third one.

XXIX*
C.T.

The maidens went back to the Lords, and gave them the pieces of cloth as proof that they had seen Tohil. The Lords tried them on and the cloths with the jaguar and the eagle did not harm them, but the horseflies and wasps of the third one stung them. They reprimanded the maidens, saying to them.:

"What kind of cloth is this that you brought? Where did you go to get it, you, mischievous ones? "

In this way the people of the tribes were overcome by Tohil.

49 C.D.

The Ahawab, the Lords, held council again to discuss what they were going to do, and they decided to declare war on Balam Quitze, Balam Ak'ab, Mahucutah, and Iqui Balam. After arming themselves they began to search for them.

The four chiefs were entrenched at the summit of Hacawitz Mountain together with their wives and sons.

50 C.D.

The people of the tribes armed themselves and their Lords put on all their war ornaments. They were bent on killing the Sacrificers and all their followers. They gathered at the foot of the mountain and slept during the night.

Balam Quitze, Balam Ak'ab, Mahucutah and Iqui Balam approached them cautiously and cut off their beards and eyelashes. They took with them the silver and jade necklaces and ornaments.

The four leaders, the Ahawab, built a fence around the town made some dolls out of rags and placed them over the fences armed with the bows and shields they had stolen from the tribes and put the silver and jade ornaments on them.

VIII*
C.T.

Balam Quitze, Balam Ak'ab, Mahucutah and Iqui Balam held council with Tohil and on his suggestion put horseflies and wasps into four gourds that they placed around the town.

The innumerable people who formed the army of the tribes attacked the town on the mountain from all sides while murmuring and yelling.

C.TC.

The people went near the town whistling and clapping their hands because they did not fear the four Ahawab, the four Lords, who were quietly watching all the movements of the tribes.

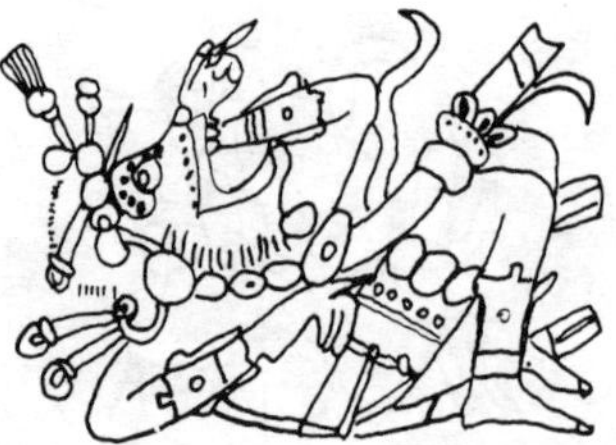

49 C.D.

50 C.D.

The Ahawab opened the four gourds and the horseflies and wasps came out in such numbers that they resembled smoke. They charged over the people and stung them on the eyes, mouth and nose, arms and legs, biting them all over their bodies.

The hideous animals buzzed in swarms and gathered over the soldiers.

42. C.D.

When the soldiers were as dizzy as drunkards they let go of the arrows and shields, scattering them all over the ground. Balam Quitze and the others grabbed some sticks and hit the soldiers, who died in great numbers. The ones who were not dead became their vassals.

In this way the tribes were overcome by our first fathers.

65 C.D.

Balam Quitze, Balam Ak'ab, Mahucutah, and Iqui Balam arranged all their affairs in preparation for their deaths because they knew that their time was near. They bade goodby to their wives and sons.

23 C.D.

Balam Quitze begot two sons: one called Cocaib and the other Cocawib, and from him descend the ones of the House of Cawec.

20 C.D.

Balam Ak'ab begot two sons, Coacul and Coacutec, and he was the forefather of those of the House of Nihaib.

XX*
C.T.

Mahucutah begot an only son, Coahaw, and from him descend those of the House of Quiche.

18. C.D.

These three begot sons, but Iqui Balam did not.

When they were all together they began to sing, weeping softly, the song called Camacu, while they bade farewell to their sons.

VII
C.T.

They said to their sons when they took leave of them:

"Heed our words. We are going back to our original towns and we shall not return. The Ahaw of the Deer, who is the symbol of leavetaking and disappearance, has already manifested himself in Heaven. Our days are numbered. Take care of your homes and country, and go once more to the place we came from."

Saying this they disappeared, and this was the end of those four Ahawab who came from the East, from the other side of the sea, and who were called the Worshipful.

31 C.D.

The sons of the Ahawab married and had descendants. When they were old, they tried to fulfill their fathers' command and went back to the East whence they had come.

The Ahaw of Tulan, in the East, was Nacxit. He exalted them, and he gave them the investiture of their Kingdoms.

When they came back they showed their people the titles and ornaments of great value that Nacxit gave them as a token of Lordship and Empire.

And they brought their art of writing and painting from Tulan.

V
C.T.

The wives of Balam Quitze, Balam Ak'ab, Mahucutah, and Iqui Balam died at Hacawitz Mountain.

As the sons of the Ahawab multiplied very rapidly, they looked for another place to live in. They inhabited another four mountains and multiplied themselves there, too, and married off their sons and daughters. They received the presents they were given in exchange for their daughters. They ate and drank as a token of thankfulness for their descendants. And they said about the women:

"That they may have sons and daughters."

60 C.D.

They went to live at Izmachi Mountain, and there they built their structures with lime and stone.

In the fourth generation Cotuha and his adjunct Xtayul were Ahawab, and there were three Great Houses or branches: one of the Ahaw Cawec, another of the Ahaw Nihaib, and the other of the Ahaw Quiche. They were all living in peace without quarrels when the tribe of the Ilocab, envious of the others' might, wanted to have their own Ahaw, and promoted war against Cotuha in order to kill him.

C.TC.

But the Ahaw Cotuha gathered his soldiers and charged against them. Very few escaped. Those he took prisoners he sacrificed before the Idol.

XVII*
C.T.

Over in Izmachi there grew up in the people the custom of shedding their own blood out of fear of their God.

II
C.T.

Many people gave themselves up, falling into slavery and serfdom.

This was the beginning of the wars and dissent and the beginning of human sacrifices to the Idol.

On this occasion the Quiches reaffirmed their Empire because they had many powerful Ahawab and the tribes began to fear them.

When they were at Gumarcaah they formed twenty four Great Houses: the ones of Cawec were divided into nine Great Houses; the ones of Nihaib into nine Houses; the ones of the Ahaw Quiche into four Great Houses; the ones of Zaquic into two Great Houses.

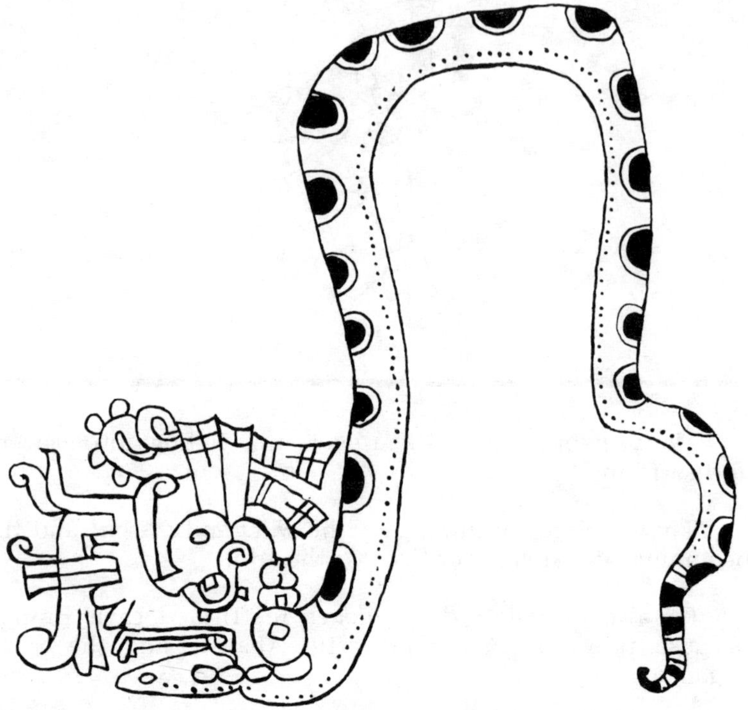

XXIV
C.T.

When all the clans were distributed among the Ahawab, the majesty and might of the Kingdom of Quiche was great. They built everything with mortar and stone.

These people were not overpowered in battles, but by the greatness of the Quiche and because of the marvels performed by the Ahawab, among which the Ahaw K'ucumatz was the greatest. He went to Heaven for seven days; for another seven days he went to Hell; for another seven days he transformed himself into a serpent;

C.TC.

for another seven days he was changed into an eagle;

47 C.D.

for another seven days he changed himself into a jaguar,

C.TC.

and during another seven days he was changed into spilled and coagulated blood.

These wonders caused much respect.

48 C.D.

During the time of the Ahaw Quik'ab, of the sixth generation, the people revolted against him because they did not want to pay tribute any longer.

48 C.D.

But Quik'ab overpowered those of Rabinal, the Cakchiqueles and the people of Zaculeu, and all were subjugated.

XXVII*
C.T.

They shot arrows at the people of the tribes who did not want to pay tribute and punished them.

47 C.D.

All men were taught to become soldiers and archers in order to have them come to battles.

60 C.D.

They appointed captains to keep watch on their frontiers and they were distributed on the mountains. The enemies they took prisoners were brought before the Ahaw Quik'ab and the Ahaw Cawizimah, of the sixth generation. With all this training they became excellent warriors, showing their dexterity with the bow and the arrow. In this way they fought with great spirit.

IX*
C.T.

The House of the God was called The Great House of Tohil.

When the Ahawab, the Lords, and the tribes went to see the Ahaw or when they went to him to pay their tribute, the first thing they did was to take their fruit offerings to the God at The Great House of Tohil.

XXXII
C.T.

The Ahawab, the Lords, were not idle; indeed they were practicing fastings and abstinence from their wives, performing penitences and prayers. They prostrated themselves while burning incense in front of their God.

All this they did on behalf of their vassals.

65 C.D.

During the time of these fastings and penitences they ate only fruit without tasting their corn cakes.

Thirteen of the Lords were fasting, and eleven were praying at the same time.

Great was the fast they held on behalf of their vassals as indication of dominance over them. Day and night they prayed. They cried and asked favors for their people and for their Kingdom.

During those days they did not sleep with their wives.

XXX*
C.T.

Bowing before the God, they said this prayer:

"Oh, Thou, Beauty of the Day! Thou, Hurakan, Thou, Heart of Heaven and of Earth! Thou, Giver of our glory and of our sons and daughters! We pray Thee to multiply Thy sustainers and the ones who invoke Thee on the road, on the rivers, in the ravines, under the trees and vines. Give them sons and daughters. That they do not find disgrace or misfortune, do not let them be deceived, nor let them stumble or fall. Do not allow any court to judge them. Do not let them fall when they walk up and down the road; put them on the good road, that nothing strike them. Do not let them have any misfortune or disgrace.

(to be continued)

"God, grant good customs to the ones who must sustain Thee! Oh, Thou, UC'UX CAH, Heart of Heaven, UC'UX ULEW, Heart of the Earth! Oh, Thou, Bundle of Glory and Majesty! Thou, Tohil, Awilix, Hacawitz, Womb of Heaven, Womb of the Earth! Oh, Thou, Who art the Four Corners of the Earth, let there be Peace in Thy Presence! Oh, God! "

The prayers, fasting and penitences were the price paid by the Ahawab, the Lords, for their power and authority. And the succession to the throne was by twos in order to share the burden of the tribes.

XIX*
C.T.

Balam Quitze, Balam Ak'ab, Mahucutah, and Iqui Balam were the first fathers and grandfathers of all of us, the Quiches; and our first mothers and grandmothers, their wives, were Caha Paluna, Chomiha, Tzununiha, and K'aquixaha.

This is the history of the Quiche country and of what happened there. This has been written because the ancient book where it was recorded was lost and there is no other place to read all this.

In this way everything ended concerning the Kingdom of Quiche, now called Santa Cruz, the Holy Cross.

VOCABULARY

ah.- Particle that is attached to a noun, and means *the one who makes* or *the one who works;* or *rank;* or *place of origin.*

AHALK'ANA. Lord of Xibalba. With Ahalpuh their job was to produce swellings on men, matter on their limbs, and yellow tint on their faces. This sickness was called *their yellowness.*

AHALMES. *The one who makes refuse.* One of the Lords of Xibalba. With Ahaltok'ob their job was to pinch men, make them encounter evil or to die face-down, or on the door of their houses, or behind them.

AHALPUH. *The one who makes matter.* (see. AHALK'ANA, matter)

AHALTOK'OB. *The one who makes misery* (see: AHALMES)

ahaw. *Lord.* From *ah* and *aw* meaning the chain with a jewel as a pendant which the Lords wore. *The one with the chain or jewel.*

ahawab. Plural of *ahaw.*

ants 1. They carried Zipacna's cuttings from his hair and fingernails to deceive the Four Hundred Youths.
2. They cut the flowers in the garden of Xibalba under the orders of Hun Ahpu and Xbalamque.
3. *acromirmex lundi,* ant that cuts the leaves. The biggest measures from 7 to 9 mm., the smaller only from 2 to 4 mm.

armadillo. (see: IBOY)

AWILIX. ONE OF THE GODS OF THE QUICHES. Balam Ak'ab carried his image in a *cacaxte* (see) on his back.

axe 1. Hun Ahpu and Xbalamque used an axe when they cut down the trees and vines to prepare their cornfield to sow corn, (see)
2. The axes were made of stone.

BALAM AK'AB. *Jaguar of the Night.* One of the first four men to be created. His wife was Chomiha. (see) First father and grandfather of the House of Nihaib. (see: NIHAIB)

BALAM QUITZE. *Jaguar of Sweet Laughter.* One of the first four men to be created. His wife was *Caha Paluna.* (see) Founders of the House of Cawec. (see; *Cawec)*

ball. It was made of solid rubber from the sap of the rubber tree. (see: rubber)

ball court. (In Copan "It consisted of a playing alley with three markers, the sloping sides, and the temples on each side." (Plate 6a. p. 64-65, Thompson, 1970)
2. "...A game something like basketball was played in these courts. Instead of baskets at the two ends of the court, however, there were two stone rings, one let into each of the long facing walls at their middle points..." (Morley, 1947, p. 326).
3. Hun Hunahpu and Wukub Hunahpu played ball in their ball court, and the Ahawab of Xibalba heard them.

4. Hun Ahpu and Xbalamque played ball in the court of their fathers. When they went to Xibalba, they played in the ball court of the Ahawab.

ball game. They played ball by bouncing it off the hips through a stone ring placed on a wall.

"...(This) Maya game combined features of basketball and soccer. Using elbows, knees, and hips, but no hands, players sought to drive a solid rubber ball throught a stone ring high on the opponents' wall. Tradition says spectators vanished when a player scored: the feat made him winner of their clothes and jewelry." (*Indians of the Americas*, National Geographic Society, Washington, D. C. 1955. p. 202).

bat. (see: SOTZ)

beans 1. Food allotted to the mouse by Hun Ahpu and Xbalamque. (see: CH'O)

2. Of the *gender phaseoulus*. There are different species: the white, the black, the red, the yellow, etc.

blood 1. The name *Xquic*, (see) means *blood*.

2. The name *Cuchumaquic* means *Gathered blood*. (see: Cuchumaquic)

3. The Ahaw K'ucumatz was changed into spilled and coagulated blood during seven days. (see: K'UCUMATZ)

blood-letting 1. "Blood-letting and scarification played a leading part in religious observance. Blood was drawn from the ears (especially the lobes), the nose, the forehead, the cheeks, the lower lips, the elbows, arms, thighs and legs, and the private parts. The blood thus obtained, as well as that of sacrificial victims, human as well as animal, was liberally sprinkled over their idols". (Morley, 1947. p.218)

2. "The perforation and cutting instruments used in these blood-letting rites were the bony snout of the swordfish, the barb of the sting-ray, fishspines, thorns of the gourd tree, and knives and blades made of flint, obsidian, bones, and shell." (Morley, 1947. p.218)

blowguns. 1. They were made from a part of a cane, from knot to knot. By blowing strongly, it was possible to shoot mud pellets or arrows throught it.

2. (see: mud pellet 1,2)

3. Hun Ahpu and Xbalamque chased birds with their blowguns for their brothers Hun Batz and Hun Chowen.

4. The two youths Hun Ahpu and Xbalamque used only their breath in their blowguns when they were chasing birds in company of Cab Rakan.

5. Hun Ahpu and Xbalamque amused themselves shooting with their blowguns while they simulated work in their cornfield.

6. Hun Ahpu and Xbalamque shot the Hawk (see) with their blowguns. (see: rubber 1)

7. Hun Ahpu and Xbalamque went to the road of Xibalba carrying their blowguns, and crossed the river of matter and the river of blood on their blowguns.

8. Hun Ahpu and Xbalamque slept inside their blowguns when they were in the HOUSE OF BATS (see: CAMASOTZ, HOUSE OF BATS)

bowl 1. The bowls struck the faces of the men of wood when they were punished by the HEART OF HEAVEN. (see: HURAKAN)

2. The Indians use earthen bowls as cups and kitchenware.

CAB RAKAN 1. *Two legs or two feet.* Second son of Wukub K'aquix and Chimalmat. He was very proud of himself. He caused the small and the big mountains to tremble. (see: Wukub K'aquix, Chimalmat, Zipacna)

2. Today Indians call an earth tremor: *cab rakan,* and earthquakes: *nimalaj cab rakan. (nimalaj:* greatest)

cacao 1. Its seeds were destined as food for the mouse. (see)

2. *theobroma cacao.* Chocolate is made from its seeds, also cacao pomade.

cacaxte. A kind of wooden box or crate to carry fruit on the back of a porter, suspended with the aid of a tumpline. (see)

CACULHA HURAKAN. *Lightning with one leg.* First manifestation of HURAKAN. (see).

CAHA PALUNA: *Standing Water Falling from Above,* wife of *Balam Quitze.* (see *Cawec, Balam Quitze).*

CAKCHIQUEL 1. The *Cakchiquel* tribes were with the *Quiches* when they came out of Tulan.

2. Protected by smoke, the *Cakchiquels* stole the fire from the *Quiches.*

3. They were rebels against the *Quiches,* but were subdued by Quik'ab.

CAMACU. Farewell and death song of the first four men when they bade goodby to their wives and sons.

CAMALOTZ. An animal which cut off the heads of the men of wood when they were punished by the *Heart of Heaven.* (see: HURAKAN)

CAMASOTZ. *Bat of Death.* It cut off Hun Ahpu's head when the two youths were prisoners in the HOUSE OF BATS.

cantil 1. One of the animals created by the Creators and Makers to guard the mountains.

2. *agkistrodon bilineatus.* A poisonous snake. It inhabits the coast of the Pacific Ocean from sea level up to 600 m. elevation.

CAWEC. Great Quiche House of Lords, founded by Balam Quitze and Caha Paluna. (see)

CAWISIMAH. Lord adjunct to Quik'ab (see) of the House of Cawec, VII generation.

centipede. (see: *Xtzul)*

COACUL. One of the two sons of Balam Ak'ab and Chomiha. His brother was *Cocawib.* From the House of Nihaib. (see)

COACUTEC. (see: COACUL)

COAHAW. Only son of Mahucutah and Tzununiha. From the House of Ahaw Quiche. (see)

coati 1. *Nasua narica.*

2. Hun Ahpu and Xbalamque could not catch the coati.

3. One of the animals which answered Xbalamque's call.

He wanted to select among the animals the one that could serve as Hun Ahpu's head. (see: *coc)*

coc. *The tortoise.* Hun Ahpu's head was made from the tortoise shell when his own was cut off by *Camasotz.* (see: tortoise, CAMASOTZ)

COCAIB. One of the two sons born to Balam Quitze and Caha Paluna. His brother was *Cocawib.* From the House of Cawec. (see)

COCAWIB. (see: COCAIB)

copal. (see: *pom)*

corn 1. Food for the mouse given by Hun Ahpu and Xbalamque. (see: mouse)

2. The Creators and Makers made man from the meal of the yellow and the white corn. (see: Xmucane, Hoh)

3. *Zea mays.*

corn beverage 1. The FOUR HUNDRED YOUTHS (see) got drunk with this intoxicating drink when they celebrated Zipacna's death.

2. This fermented beverage is made of yellow corn and other ingredients.

corn cakes 1. *Tortillas* or flat corn cakes made from the meal of corn half cooked with lime. They are made by hand and finish cooking on earthen griddles. Eaten with black beans they constitute the daily fare of the Indians.

2. The Great Lords could not eat *tortillas* when they were fasting. (see: tropical fruits)

corn field 1. Hun Batz and Hun Chowen, Hun Ahpu and Xbalamque planted corn in their corn fields.

2. Xmucane sent Xquic to the corn field of her grandsons Hun Batz and Hun Chowen to harvest a net full of corn. (see: Xquic)

COTCOWACH. An animal which gouged out the eyes of the men of wood when they were punished by the *Heart of Heaven.* (see: HURAKAN)

COTUHA. Lord of the House of Cawec, fourth generation. His adjunct was Xtayul. (see: IZMACHI, CAWEC)

COTZBALAM. This animal ate the meat of the men of wood when they were punished by the HEART OF HEAVEN. (see: HURAKAN)

COY 1. *The monkey.* The men of wood were transformed into monkeys because they did not remember the Creators and Makers.

2. Hun Batz and Hun Chowen were transformed into monkeys because they behaved badly against Hun Ahpu and Xbalamque.
3. *ateles geoffroyi.* The Guatemalan species is the *ateles geoffroyi pan Schlegel.* They inhabit Alta Verapaz and the mountains in the central part of Guatemala.

coyote. (see: UTIW)

creation of man. The Creators and Makers made various attempts to create the being destined to worship them:
1. The first attempt was the creation of animals, but they could not praise them.
2. The second time they made man of mud, but he dissolved in water, and he was destroyed. (see: mud)
3. The third instance was when they made man of wood. He could reproduce himself and could speak, but he forgot to praise the Creators. He was punished by the HEART OF HEAVEN who sent a heavy rain of resin and tar to deluge him.
4. The fourth and last attempt was successful. Man was created from corn. (see: XMUCANE 3, QUEL)

CUCHUMAQUIC. *Gathered blood.* One of the Lords at Xibalba. Xquic's father. His companion was Xiquiripat. Their job was to cause blood illness to men. (see: XQUIC).

CUX 1. *The weasel.* A dance that Hun Ahpu and Xbalamque performed at Xibalba.
2.*mustela frenata.*

C'UCH 1. *The buzzard.* It blackened the sky four times by opening its wings when Xbalamque was carving Hun Ahpu's head.
2. In quiche, *c'uch* is the word for buzzard, but by mistake Ximenez wrote *wuch*, opposum: *didelfis marsupialis.* The buzzard is *ciragups atratus.* Its favorite food is filth and putrified meat.

CHAMIABAK. *Bone rod.* With Chamiaholom they were constables of Xibalba; their rods were only bones, and their job was to make men thin and lean, and, when they were skeletons to assure that they died with their stomachs attached to their backs.

CHAMIAHOLOM *Skull rod.* (see: CHAMIABAK)

CHIMALMAT. Wukub K'aquix's wife and mother of Zipacna and Cab Rakan. (see: WUKUB K'AQUIX, ZIPACNA, CAB RAKAN)

CHIPI CACULHA. *The younger of the lightnings.* Second manifestation of Hurakan. (see: CACULHA HURAKAN, RAXA CACULHA, HURAKAN)

CHITIC. *The one who walks on stilts.* Dance by Hun Ahpu and Xbalamque at Xibalba.

CHOMIHA. *Beautiful and Chosen Water.* One of the four first women who were created. Balam Ak'ab was her husband. (see)

CH'O 1. *The mouse.* The only animal that Hun Ahpu and Xbalamque caught. It revealed to them their destiny. The youths alloted the mouse its food: pepper seeds, corn, beans, cacao and the foods kept in the houses. (see: garret 2)
2. Of the *mus* gender.

deer 1. One of the animals created to be the guardians of the woods.
2. One of the animals that Hun Ahpu and Xbalamque could not catch.
3. The Sacrificers searched for the females of the deer and of birds, to offer them to the idols.
4. The Lord of the Deer, symbol of farewell, appeared to the first four men when their time to die came.
5. *odocoileus virginianus.* In Quiche: *quiej.*

dog 1. The dogs rebelled against the men of wood when these were punished by the HEART OF HEAVEN. (see: HURAKAN)
2. Hun Ahpu and Xbalamque quartered a dog and revived it when they were practicing their magic powers at Xibalba.
3. According to Fuentes y Guzman "the silent dogs good to eat" were the *tepezcuintles (nelson paca)* a South American animal resembling a sucking pig. Truthfully there were different kinds of dogs as testified in the drawings of the Codices. (in this text see pages: 14, 59, 99)
4. *canis familiaris.*

eagle 1. Balam Ak'ab painted an eagle on the cloth that he gave to the maidens.
2. K'ucumatz changed himself into an eagle for seven days.
3. *harpia harpija.*

earthen griddles. 1. Kitchenware that rebelled against men of wood when these were punished by the HEART OF HEAVEN. (see: HURAKAN)
2. It is an earthen flat disc which is placed on three stones over the fire to cook *tortillas.* (see: corn cakes)

earthen jars 1. Large jars of clay that the Indians use to carry water and to keep it in the houses.
2. Xan, the Mosquito, bored a hole into Xmucane's earthen jar at the command of Hun Ahpu and Xbalamque.
3. Kitchenware that rebelled against men of wood when they were punished by the HEART OF HEAVEN. (see: earthen griddles)

fire 1. Hun Ahpu and Xbalamque made a fire to roast a bird covered with clay that Cab Rakan ate. He lost his strenght because of it, and was overcome by the two youths.
2. The fire was created by Tohil. He gave it to the Quiches. (see: TOHIL 2)
3. The Cakchiquel people stole the fire from the Quiches using the smoke as a screen.

firefly. Hun Ahpu and Xbalamque placed fireflies at the end of their tobacco cigars to make believe they were burning.

fire stones. 1. The Indians use three stones on the fire to place their cooking pots and griddles.
2. The fire stones rebelled against the men of wood, because of the great pains they suffered when placed on the fire.

FOUR HUNDRED YOUTHS. They were killed by Zipacna, and went to heaven where they were placed as stars. The Indians called them *Motz*, the *Huddle.* (The Pleiades)

garret 1. The space of a house directly under the roof.

2. Hun Ahpu and Xbalamque's fathers hid the implements of the ball game pertaining to them, in the garret of their house. The mouse revealed the place to the two youths. (see: CH'O)

gourd 1. (see: horsefly)

2. The Tucur, the Owls, carried the red sap in a gourd. It coagulated in a heart-shaped clot, instead of Xquic's heart. They brought it to the Lords of Xibalba.

3. Hun Ahpu and Xbalamque offered the Lords of Xibalba four gourds full of flowers.

4. *legenaria clavata, legenaria vulgaris, a cucurbitaceous.* The Indians use them to carry warm beverages because the gourds keep the temperature for a long time.

gourd tree 1. Hun Hunahpu's head was transformed into a gourd when it was placed on the tree by the road at the command of Hun Came and Wukub Came, Lords of Xibalba.

2. *crescentia cujete.* The Indians make household utensils from its fruit. There are other species: *crescentia alata,* its fruit is called: *morro.*

gray fox. (see: YAK)

grinding stones 1. "You tormented us, now we shall atrike you", said the grinding stones to the men of wood when the HEART OF HEAVEN decided to destroy them. (see: *Holi...,* HURAKAN)

2. Special stones where the Indians grind the corn to make the meal for the *tortillas.* (see)

GUMARCAAH. One of the capitals of the Quiches.

HACAWITZ 1. God of the Quiches. His image was the third to come out of Tulan and was carried by Mahucutah on his back in a *cacaxte.* (see)

2. Name of the mountain where Mahucutah hid the image of Hacawitz before the appearance of the sun.

3. On the same Hacawitz Mountain the people saw the sun rise.

4. When the tribes of the Quiche people were living on Hacawitz Mountain the first four chiefs fortified it against the attack of the hostile tribes. To overcome them they used gourds full of wasps and horseflies as bombs. (see: horsefly)

hawk. (see: Xic)

HEART OF HEAVEN. (see: HURAKAN)

hens 1. Animals which demanded to know why they were eaten by the men of wood.

2. *meleagris gallopavo,* the turkey. Origin of the domestic turkey. These were the *hens* the Spaniards found in Central America and Mexico, and called them *hens of the country.*

HOH 1. One of the four animals which showed the Creators and Makers the place where the white and the yellow corn grew. With these two kinds of corn, the gods made the flesh and substance of man. (see: *quel*, *utiw*, *yak*, Xmucane 3)

2. *corvus corax.* The raven.

holi, holi, huqui, huqui. Sound of the grinding stones when the corn is crushed to make cornmeal.

honey combs. The first four men brought to their wives and sons honey combs, horseflies and wasps to eat. (see: horsefly, wasps)

horsefly 1. The first four leaders of the Quiche tribes filled gourds with wasps and horseflies to be used as bombs in battle. (see: HACAWITZ 4)

2. *tabanus costalis.* Their prickings torment the animals.

3. (see: honey combs)

HOUSE OF BATS. Place of punishment at Xibalba, full of bats.

HOUSE OF COLD. Place of punishment at Xibalba, so cold that it was also called the House of Shivering.

HOUSE OF DARKNESS. Place of punishment at Xibalba, full of gloom.

HOUSE OF FIRE. Place of punishment at Xibalba. The fire filled it.

HOUSE OF OBSIDIAN KNIVES. Place of punishment at Xibalba. So many knives were there that they grated against each other.

HOUSE OF JAGUARS. Place of punishment at Xibalba, in which were countless numbers of jaguars.

hun. *One.* Number used in several names.

HUN AHPU. Xbalamque's brother, sons of Hun Hunahpu and Xquic. (see) The young girl conceived them when the skull of Hun Hunahpu spit saliva into the palm of her hand. When the youths died they were placed —one, as the Sun and the other, as the Moon.

HUN AHPU COY. Hun Ahpu's monkey. A song that Hun Ahpu and Xbalamque sang to attract their brothers, who were changed into monkeys.

HUN BATZ. *One thread.* Hun Chowen's brother, sons of Hun Hunahpu and Xbakiyalo. (see: Hun Chowen, Xbakiyalo)

HUN CAME. *One death.* He and Wukub Came were the most important Lords at Xibalba. They were great judges. The other Lords obeyed and served them.

HUN CHOWEN. *One who is in order.* Hun Batz was his brother. They were changed into monkeys because they were proud, and they behaved badly toward their brothers Hun Ahpu and Xbalamque. (see: Hun Batz, Xbakiyalo)

HUN HUNAHPU. *One hunter with a blowgun.* Wukub Hunahpu was his brother, sons of Xpiyacoc and Xmucane. He was Hun Batz and Hun Chowen's father by his wife Xbakiyalo (see) and of Hun Ahpu and Xbalamque by the maiden Xquic. (see)

HURAKAN. *One foot.* Also called the Heart of Heaven, UC'UX CAH. He had three different appearances: CACULHA HURAKAN, CHIPI CACULHA AND RAXA CACULHA. (see)

IBOY 1. *Armadillo.* Dance by Hun Ahpu and Xbalamque at Xibalba.
2. *dasypus novemcinctus fenestratus Peters.* Lives in almost all parts of Guatemala.

ICOK'IJ 1. The star all the tribes saw before the sun rose.
2. The morning star when it precedes the sun, and the evening star when it follows the sunset. It can be identified easily as Venus.

ILOCAB. One of the Quiche factions.

IQUI BALAM. *Jaguar of the Moon.* One of the first four men to be created. His wife was K'aquixaha. (see) No issue.

IZMACHI. Mountain where the Quiches lived. There they founded their capital, and their buildings were made of stone and lime, during the IV generation under Cotuha and Xtayul. (see)

jade necklaces. The chiefs of the tribes who made war againts the first four men put them on to go into battle.

jaguar 1. One of the first animals formed by the Creators and Makers as guardian of the woods.
2. *Balam* in Quiche. Part of the following names: Balam Quitze, Balam Ak'ab, Iqui Balam. (see)
3. The Sacrificers, leaders of the Quiche, imitated the roaring of the jaguar when they kidnapped the people of the tribes.
4. One of the animals that Hun Ahpu and Xbalamque could not catch.
5. The House of Jaguars, a place of punishment at Xibalba, was full of these animals.
6. Balam Ak'ab painted a jaguar on the cloth that he gave to the maidens.
7. K'ucumatz, famous Quiche Lord, could change himself into a jaguar for seven days.
8. *felix onca.* Jaguar or tiger of the Americas.

K'AQUIX 1. *The Macaw.* (lit.: red feather) Part of the name ***Wukub K'aquix:*** Seven Macaw. And part of the name ***K'aquixaha:*** Macaw Water, Iqui Balam's wife. (see) Tucum Balam.
2. Hun Ahpu and Xbalamque took two feathers from the tail of the macaw, and placed them on the pine sticks to make believe they were burning them when they were prisoners in the House of Darkness. (see).
3. *ara macao, ara ararauna,* are the most known species: the red and the blue ones with yellow feathers. They have and enormous beak, long tail, and brilliant colors.

K'AQUIXAHA. *Macaw Water.* One of the first four women to be created by the Creators and Makers. Iqui Balam's wife. (see) No issue.

K'UCUMATZ 1. *Lord Quetzal Serpent.* (from the Quiche: ***K'uk',*** quetzal; *cumatz*, serpent). Creator and Maker. "Father and Mother of everything that is in the water. He was in brilliant light, ornamented and hidden among green feathers (which were the ones from the *quetzal* used by the Lords as symbols of Majesty and Greatness). Because of that He was called K'UCUMATZ, and Strong and Learned Serpent for His great knowledge and understanding. And He is also known as the HEART OF HEAVEN (see: HURAKAN) because He is there and there He lives". (Ximenez). He is identified with the Mexican QUETZALCOATL.

2. Great Lord famous for his deeds. He used to go down to Hell, and to go up to Heaven. He could change himself into a serpent, into an eagle, into a jaguar, or into spilled blood. He governed with his adjunct Cotuha. Fifth generation, House of Cawec. (see)

K'UK'. *Quetzal. pharomachrus mocinno mocinno De La Llave*, is the accepted scientific name of the Guatemalan quetzal, our national bird, emblem of liberty. (see: K'ucumatz). It inhabits cold regions from 6,000 to 10,000 feet elevation. Because of its beauty it has been the victim of intense harassment and it has taken refuge in dense jungles. It lives in high trees and eats fruit, especially the one called "little avocado." The male is magnificent: the feathers of tail, head, breast and upper body are irisdiscent green and blue. The abdomen and the feathers that cover the under side of the taild are red. The feathers on the tail are three feet long. The female is inferior in beauty.

macaw. (see: *K'aquix)*

MAHUCUTAH. *Not Brushed.* One of the first four men that were created. His wife was Tzununiha. Founders of the House of Ahaw Quiche. (see)

matter 1. *pus.* The road to Xibalba was reached by crossing a river of matter.

2. Ahalkana and Ahalpuh, Lords of Xibalba, produced matter on men.

monkey. (see: *Coy)*

mosquito. (see: *Xan)*

MOTZ. *The Huddle,* the group of the Pleiades. The FOUR HUNDRED YOUTHS killed by Zipacna were placed in Heaven as a cluster of stars, when Hun Ahpu and Xbalamque were placed as the Sun and the Moon. (see: FOUR HUNDRED YOUTHS)

mouse. (see: *Ch'o)*

mud 1. The first man was made of mud, but he dissolved in water.

2. (see: rain 3)

mud pellet 1. Hun Ahpu blew a mud pellet with his blowgun at Wukub K'aquix when he was eating the yellow berries on his tree. (see: blowguns)

2. The pellets are made of clay or mud, and are used as ammunition for blowguns and slingshots.

NACXIT. Great Lord, governor of Tulan, in the East. He gave their titles of Lordship to the sons of the first Quiche Lords.

NICAHTACAH. Name of the god whose image Iqui Balam took out of Tulan on his back in a *cacaxte.* (see)

NIHAIB. One of the Great Quiche Houses. Their ancestors: Balam Ak'ab and Chomiha. (see)

obsidian knives. The House of Knives was full of them. (see)

owl. (see: *Pubuy, Tucur)*

painting 1. (see: writing)

2. Hun Hunahpu taught his sons Hun Batz and Hun Chowen how to paint.

parrot. (see: *Queletzu)*

PATAN. *Tumpline.* (see) Lord of Xibalba, Xic's companion. Their job was to cause sudden death to the ones who died on the roads, spitting blood. Part of their job was to pummel people's hearts when they died on the roads and to cause them to have blood stools.

pataxte 1. One of the foods that Hun Ahpu and Xbalamque gave to the mouse. (see)

2. *theobroma bicolor.* A kind of cacao tree in Central America. The seeds are processed as the cacao beans, but are less appreciated.

peccary 1. One of the animals that Hun Ahpu and Xbalamque could not catch.

2. One of the animals that Xbalamque called in order to select one to be carved as Hun Ahpu's head.

3. *tayassu peccari.* They live in Mexico, Guatemala, and Honduras.

pepper. 1. Hun Ahpu and Xbalamque allotted pepper seeds to serve as food for the mouse. (see)

2. *capsicum annuum.*

perroquet. (see: *Quel)*

pine sticks 1. Hun Hunahpu and Wukub Hunahpu were defeated by the Lords of Xibalba when they burned their pitch pine sticks in the House of Darkness. (see) But Hun Ahpu and Xbalamque placed macaw feathers on theirs to prevent them from burning.

2. *pinus Hartvegii.*

planting stick. 1. Hun Ahpu and Xbalamque used a planting stick to till the earth and sow corn.

2. The point of the stick was hardened by burning it.

plates. Kitchenware that rebelled against men of wood when they were punished by the HEART OF HEAVEN. (see: HURAKAN)

pom 1. *euphorbia heterophylla.* Resin still used by the Indians as incense in their religious ceremonies.

2. The first four Lords that were created burned *pom* when the sun appeared.

3. Grandmother Xmucane burned *pom* in the middle of the house when the canes that her grandsons Hun Ahpu and Xbalamque planted sprouted again after drying up.

4. The Lords burned *pom* in front of Tohil when in worship.

pot. The earthen pots complained to the wooden men because they suffered burns from the fire over which they were placed.

PUHUY 1. *The Owl.* One of the dances by Hun Ahpu and Xbalamque at Xibalba.

2. *strix flammea, strix passerina.*

puma 1. One of the first animals to be created by the Makers as guardian of the woods.

2. The Sacrificers imitated the roaring of the puma to deceive the people of the tribes.

3. One of the animals that Hun Ahpu and Xbalamque could not catch.

4. The Ahawab of Xibalba, the Lords of Hell, and Hun Ahpu and Xbalamque, once played with a puma's head, instead of a rubber ball, in their competitive ball games.

5. *felix concolor.* The lion of the Americas. The Guatemalan puma or lion is: *felix concolor mayensis Nelson and Goldman.* In Quiche: *cob.*

QUEL 1. *The parrakeet.* One of the animals that revealed to the Creators and Makers the place where corn could be found in order to make the flesh of man from it. (see: *hob, utiw, yak, Xmucane* 3)

2. Belongs to the order of the *psitaceas.*

QUELETZU 1. *The Parrot.* The first animal to sing when the sun rose from the East.

2. Order of the *psitaceas.*

QUETZAL. (see: *k'uk')*

QUICHE. The factions of the Quiches were: the Tamub, the Ilocab, and the one of the Ahaw Quiche. Tohil was their god when they came out of Tulan.

QUICRE. One of the Lords of Xibalba. Hun Ahpu and Xbalamque hailed him when Xan, the Mosquito, revealed his name to them. His companion was Quicrixkak.

QUICRIXKAK. (see: *Quicre)*

QUICXIC. (see: XIC)

QUIEJ. (see: DEER)

QUIK'AB. Powerful Lord of the VII generation, House of Cawec. His adjunct was Cawisimaj.

rabbit 1. One of the animals that Hun Ahpu and Xbalamque could not catch. (see: *tomato)*

2. *sylvilagus floridanus*, the cottontail rabbit.

RABINAL. Indian tribe which joined the Quiche when they came out of Tulan.

rains 1. A heavy rain of resin and tar fell from Heaven to deluge the men of wood.

2. The first fire that Tohil created was drenched and put out by a heavy shower of rain and hail.

3. The people of the tribes started to follow the footprints of the Sacrificers when it began to rain, and there was so much mud that they could not continue the search.

RAXA CACULHA. *Green Lightning* or *Very Beautiful Lightning.* Third aspect of HURAKAN. (see)

red beans. (see: *tzite*, soothsayer)

road. The road to Xibalba was a difficult one: Hun Ahpu and Xbalamque had to descend the steep steps. Then they had to cross a river of blood and one of matter. Then they came to a crossroads of four roads: one was black, the other white, another red, and the last one yellow, and they had to choose the right one to go by.

rubber 1. "The Maya played their game with a solid ball of rubber a millenium before our western civilization had any knowledge of rubber or rubber ball". (Thompson, 1970, p. 7)

2. Hun Ahpu and Xbalamque cured the eye of the Hawk with a bit of rubber from their ball.

3. From this sap of the rubber tree was made the ball with which Hun Ahpu and Xbalamque played just as their fathers did before them. (see: ball)

4. There are two species: the *castilloa elastica* or rubber tree, and the *castilloa guatemalensis*, the fine rubber.

serpent 1. One of the first animals formed by the Creators and Makers as guardian of the woods.

2. K'ucumatz, great chief of the Quiches, could transform himself into a serpent for seven days. (see: K'ucumatz 1)

slash and burn. 1. To clear the ground of brambles and bushes the Indians cut them and piled them up and burned them to prepare the field to sow corn.

2. Hun Ahpu and Xbalamque cleared their corn field, but after that all trees and bushes returned to life and were the same as before being cut down. (see) planting stick)

soothsayer 1. Xpiyacoc and Xmucane (see) were soothsayers. Xpiyacoc was *ahtzite*, the one who works with the *tzite.* Xmucane was *ahk'ij*, the one who works with the counting of days.

2. Today soothsayers are called in Quiche *ahk'ij:* from *ah* meaning *the one who works*, and *k'ij*, day (it also means *sun)*, They place the *tzite* red beans (see) in a special way and make their divinations using them combined with the counting of the twenty days of their calendar month. Their calendar year has 260 days. They have not lost the same counting of days which comes down from their ancestors, since the times before the Alvaradian era in Guatemala.

SOTZ 1. *The Bat.* There were a lot of bats in the House of Bats, a place of punishment at Xibalba. (see: *Camasotz)*

2. There are different species of the gender *Sturnira.* The, vampires, *desmodus rotundus murinus,* live from Northern Mexico to Panama.

TAMAZUL 1. *The Toad.* It swallowed the louse when it was going on its way to Hun Ahpu and Xbalamque with a message from their grandmother Xmucane. (Quiche: *xpek)*

2. It is a *batrachian.*

TAMUB. One of the Quiche factions which came out of Tulan.

TEPEW. One of the Gods, Creator and Maker.

toad. (see: *Tamazul)*

tobacco 1. When Hun Hunahpu and Wukub Hunahpu were in the House of Darkness, a place of torment at Xibalba, they burned their tobacco cigars and were conquered. But Hun Ahpu and Xbalamque, in order not to be overcome, placed a firefly on the tip of their cigars to make believe that the cigars were burning. (see: pine sticks)

2. *nicotiana tabacum.* It produces nicotine, liquid alkaloid which blackens in the air. It is toxic.

TOHIL 1. God of the Quiches. Balam Quitze carried his image out of Tulan in a *cacaxte* (see) on his back.

2. Tohil created the fire by shuffling and turning around his foot in his sandal. (see: fire 2)

tomato 1. Xbalamque induced a rabbit to take refuge behind a tomato plant in order that the Lords of Xibalba would think that it was the rubber ball.

2. *solanum lycopersicum.* Plant from Brasil, Mexico and the Antilles. The Spaniards took it to Spain and from there to the rest of Europe.

tortillas. (see: corn cakes)

tortoise 1. The animal that Xbalamque chosed for Hun Ahpu's head. (see: *coc)*

2. It is a *chelonian.*

tropical fruits 1. The Lords ate fruit when they were fasting during their worship of their gods.

2. When the tribes went to see their Ahaw to pay him their tribute, the first thing they did was to take their fruit offerings to the God at The Great House of Tohil.

3. *spondias monbin, spondias purpurea, casimiroa sapota, casimiroa edulia, byrsonima cotinifolia.* There are different species of all of them.

4. Wukub K.aquix had a tree of the last kind and its yellow berries were his food.

TUCUM BALAM. An animal that broke the bones and nerves of the men of wood, and pulverized them, when they were punished by the HEART OF HEAVEN. (see: HURAKAN)

TUCUR 1. *The Owl.* The Ahawab Tucur, the Lords Owl, were the messengers at Xibalba.
2. *family strigida;* genders *bubo* and *otus.*

TULAN OR TULA. City from which emigrated all the tribes to Guatemala. From there they brought their gods, and their art of writing and painting.

tumpline. A kind of leather band with two cords attached, serving porters to carry a load more conveniently. (see: PATAN)

tzite or red beans 1. The soothsayers Xmucane and Xpiyacoc performed their divinations with the *tzite* red beans and grains of corn to know if the men of wood were going to be the right creatures to worship the Creators.
2. *erythrina rubrinervia.* With these red beans the soothsayers of today still make their divinations. The flowers and the new green leaves are edible, but they contain a narcotic.

TZUNUNIHA. *Water of Humming-birds.* Her husband was Mahacutah. (see) She was one of the first four women to be created.

UC'UX CAH. *Heart of Heaven.* One of the names given to HURAKAN. (see)

UC'UX ULEW. HEART OF THE EARTH, one of the names given to HURAKAN. (see)

ULEW 1. *The Earth.* The Creators commanded the big animals and the small animals, the big birds and the small birds, to inhabit Ulew, the Earth.
2. Xquic went up to Ulew, the Earth, from Xibalba.
3. The word *ulew,* earth, is part of one of the names given to HURAKAN: (see) UC'UX ULEW, *Heart of the Earth.* The name ZAKULEW (see) means: White Earth.

UTIW 1. *The Coyote.* One of the four animals which told the Creators and Makers the place where they could find the white and the yellow corn to make the flesh of man. (see: *hoh, quel, yak,* Xmucane 3)
2. *canis latrans.* The piercing howl of the coyote can be heard in the Guatemalan mountains specially during moonlit nights.

vines 1. Hun Ahpu and Xbalamque cut out the vines and trees on their cornfield. The next day the vines and trees came back to life and were as before.
2. They belong to the *vitis* species, which are several.

viper 1. One of the animals created by the Makers and Creators as guardian of the woods.
2. It is a·poisonous snake.

WAC 1. *The Hawk.* It swallowed Zaquicaz, the Snake, when it was on its way to find Hun Ahpu and Xbalamque to give them Xmucane's message.

2. *accipiter nisus.*

wasps. (see: gourds, horseflies, honey combs)

weeping 1. The people of the tribes and their Ahawab wept copiously when they left Tulan.

2. Balam Quitze, Balam Ak'ab, Mahucutah and Iqui Balam burned *pom* and went dancing toward the place where the sun was appearing while they shed sweet tears of happiness.

3. The first four men to be created began to sing, weeping softly, while they bade farewell to their wives and sons just before their death.

wild cat. (see: YAK)

writing. The art of writing and painting was brought from the East by the sons of the four Worshipers when they went back to Tulan.

WUKUB. *Seven.* Number used in the names: Wukub Hunahpu, Wukub K'aquix, Wukub Came.

WUKUB CAME. *Seven Death.* (see: Hun Came)

WUKUB K'AQUIX. *Seven Macaw.* The first of the proud beings. By command of the *Heart of Heaven* (see: HURAKAN) he was punished by Hun Ahpu and Xbalamque. (see: Chimalmat, Cab Rakan, Zipacna)

WUKUB HUNPAHPU. *Seven chaser with a blowgun.* Hun Hunahpu's brother. (see).

XAN 1. *The Mosquito.* It bored a hole into granmother Xmucane's earthen jar.

2. Hun Ahpu made the mosquito from a hair off his face. He sent it to learn the names of the Lords seated at the entrance of Xibalba.

3. The mosquito is the *anopheles maculipennis.* There are different kinds. Some of them transmit malaria.

XḄAKIYALO *Bundled Bones.* Her husband was Hun Hunahpu. She died when her sons Hun Batz and Hun Chowen were changed into monkeys.

XBALAMQUE 1. (see: Hun Ahpu)

2. Xbalamque carved Hun Ahpu's head from the shell of the tortoise. (see)

3. Xbalamque cut Hun Ahpu into pieces and brought him back to life.

XIBALBA. Ximenez translated it as *Hell.*

XIC 1. *The Hawk.* Ximenez writes this name *Xic*, or *Quicxic*, Lord of Xibalba, companion of Patan. (see)

2. It is a bird of prey. *spizaetus tyrannus,* is the black hawk, which can measure up to 24 inches.

XIQUIRIPAT. Lord of Xibalbá, companion of Cuchumaquic. (see)

XMUCANE 1. Her husband was Xpiyacoc. They were Hun Hunahpu and Wukub Hunahpu's parents. Hun BAtz and Hun Chowen, Hun Ahpu and Xbalamque were their grandsons.

2. Xmucane and Xpiyacoc were consulted as soothsayers by the Creators and Makers to find out if man of wood would speak.

3. Xmucane ground the yellow corn and the white corn with which the Creators and Makers made the first four men and women. (see: *tzite*, soothsayers)

XMUCUR. *The Turtle-dove.* Hun Ahpu and Xbalamque asked it to herald the coming of their grandmother when she arrived to bring them their midday meal.

2. *streptopielia turtur, columba turtur,* gray-feathered birds, whitish underneath their body.

XPIYACOC. (see: Xmucane, soothsayer)

XQUIC. *Blood.* Cuchumaquic was her father, one of the Lords of Xibalba. Hun Hunahpu spit saliva into Xquic's hand and she conceived Hun Ahpu and Xbalamque without knowing man. (see: Hun Ahpu, corn-field 2)

XTAYUL. Lord of the IV generation, House of Cawec. He was adjunct to Cotuha. (see: Cawec, Cotuha)

XTZUL. *The Centipede.* Dance by Hun Ahpu and Xbalamque at Xibalba. The dance was as follows: One of the dancers carried a knife in his mouth. They danced revolving around to the rhythm of the tortoise shell.

2. *oruscus asellus.*

YAK 1. *The gray fox.* One of the animals that Hun Ahpu and Xbalamque could not catch.

2. One of the animals to tell the Creators and Makers where to find the white and the yellow corn to make the flesh of man. (see: *utiw, quel, hoh, Xmucane* 3)

3. *urocyon cinereoargenteus.* In Guatemala it is called the *wild cat.*

ZAKULEW. One of the tribes to rebel against Quik'ab, together with the Rabinal and the Cakchiquel tribes, and were overcome by him.

ZAQUIC. One of the Quiche factions.

ZAQUICAZ 1. *The Snake.* It swallowed the toad, Tamazul, when it was running to give the grandmother's message to Hun Ahpu and Xbalamque.

2. Snake in Quiche is *cumatz*, but the proper name of this one was Zaquicaz.

ZIPACNA. Wukub K'aquix and Chimalmat's first born, another of the proud beings. He used to make mountains in one night. (see: WUKUB K'AQUIX, CHIMALMAT, CAB RAKAN)

BIBLIOGRAPHY

BASSETA, Fray Domingo. Vocabulario de lengua Quiché, 1698. Manuscript. (microfilm copy).

BRASSEUR DE BOURBOURG, Charles Etienne. *Manuscript. Troano.* Etude sur les système graphique et la langue des mayas. Paris, 1869. Tome premier.

CABRERA, Angel. *Zoología pintoresca.* Ramón Sopena, Barcelona, 1954.

CODEX CORTESIANUS. Number 1 copy from the edition of 500 numbered copies printed in Madrid in 1892. Photochromolithographic reproduction.

CODEX DRESDENSIS. (see: Gates, William).

CODEX PERESIANUS. Manuscrit hiératique des anciens indiens de L'Amerique Centrale conservé a la Bibliothéque Nationale de Paris. Avec une introduction par Leon de Rosny. Seconde edition imprimée en noir. Paris, 1888.

CODEX TROANUS. (see: Brasseur de Bourbourg).

CONTRERAS R., J. Daniel. *Breve Historia de Guatemala,* con ilustraciones y un mapa de lugares arqueológicos. Segunda edición. Ministerio de Educación Pública, Guatemala, 1961.

FONT QUER, P. *Diccionario de Botánica.* Editorial Labor, Barcelona, 1956.

FUENTES Y GUZMAN, Francisco Antonio. *Recordación Florida.* Edición conforme al códice del siglo XVII, cuyo original se conserva en el Archivo de la Municipalidad de Guatemala. Sociedad de Geografía e Historia. Guatemala, 1932-33.

GATES, William. *The Dresden Codex.* Reproduced from tracings of the original. Colorings finished by hand. The Maya Society at the Johns Hopkins University, Baltimore, 1932. (Maya Society Publication No. 2).

GUZMAN, PANTALEON. *Libro intitulado Compendio en lengua Cakchiquel,* en doce tratados. 1704. Manuscript. (microfilm copy).

HERNANDEZ SPINA, Vicente. *Apuntes del idioma Kiche.* 1854. Manuscript. (microfilm copy).

IBARRA, Jorge A. *Apuntes de historia natural y mamíferos de Guatemala.* Editorial del Ministerio de Educación Pública, Guatemala, 1959.

Historia natural y pronatura. Revista p. 18. Guatemala, No. 4, enero 1966.

MATA GAVIDIA, José. *Anotaciones de Historia Patria Centroamericana.* Editorial Cultural Centroamericana. Guatemala, 1953.

MORLEY, Sylvanus G. *The Ancient Maya.* Stanford University Press, California, 1946.

NATIONAL GEOGRAPHIC SOCIETY. *Indiàns of the Americas, A* color illustrated record. Washington, D.C., 1955.

POPOL VUH. Antiguas historias de los Indios Quichés de Guatemala. Ilustradas con dibujos de los Códices Mayas. Advertencia, versión y vocabulario de Albertina Saravia E. (c) 1965. 11a. ed. Editorial PORRUA, S.A. México, 1976. (Colección "Sepan Cuántos..." No. 36).

POPOL VUH O LIBRO SAGRADO. The Sanborn manuscript. (Translation from French to Spanish by an anonymous translator, from the Popol Vuh by Brasseur de Bourbourg). Peabody Museum, Cambridge, Mass.

POPOL VUH. *Le livre sacré et les mythes de l'antiquité Américaine,* avec les livres heroiques et historiques des Quichés. Par l'abbé Charles Etienne Brasseur de Bourbourg. Arthur Bertrand, ëditeur. Paris, 1861.

POPOL VUH. Las antiguas historias del Quiché, traduidas del texto original, con una introducción y notas por Adrián Recinos. Fondo de Cultura Económica, México, 1947.

POPOL VUH. The Sacred Book of the Ancient Quiché Maya. English versión by Delia Goetz and Sylvanus G. Morley from the translation of Adrian Recinos. University of Oklahoma Press, Norman 1950.

POPOL VUH translated by Fray Francisco Ximenez. (see: Ximenez, Fray Francisco).

THOMPSON, J. Eric S. *The rise and fall of Maya Civilization.* Second edition, enlarged. Third printing. University of Oklahoma Press, Norman, 1970.

VELASQUEZ. A new pronouncing dictionay of the SPANISH AND ENGLISH LANGUAGES. Compiled by Mariano Velásquez. (c) 1942 by D. Appleton-Century Company, Inc. Wilcox & Follet Company, New York, 1948.

VICO, Fray Domingo. *Vocabulario quiché-cakchiquel* (attributed to Vico) Manuscript. (microfilm copy).

XIMENEZ, Fray Francisco. *Historia de la Provincia de San Vicente de Chiapa y Guatemala.* Sociedad de Geografía e Historia, Guatemala, 1929.

Historias de los indios de esta provincia de Guatemala traducido de la lengua quiché en la castellana para más comodidad de los ministros del Santo Evangelio, por el R.P.F. Francisco Ximenez, cura doctrinero por el real patronato del pueblo de Santo Tomás Chuila. (paleography by Albertina Saravia, 1962).

Primera parte del Tesoro de las lenguas cakchiquel, quiché y tzutuhil en que las dichas lenguas se traducen en la nuestra española. Manuscript. (microfilm copy).